COMPLETE
GUIDE
TO
OUTBOARD
ENGINES

JOHN FLEMING

Editor: John P. O'Connor, Jr.

Bristol Fashion Publications
Harrisburg, Pennsylvania

Complete Guide To Outboard Engines, By John Fleming

Published by Bristol Fashion Publications

Copyright © 2000 by John Fleming. All rights reserved.

ISBN: 1-892216-31-0
LCCN: 00-131358

Contribution acknowledgments

Inside Graphics: By the author or as noted from Mercury and OMC.
Cover Design: John P. Kaufman
Cover Photo: Mercury Marine

Complete Guide To Outboard Engines, By John Fleming

DEDICATION

To my daughters, Cynthia Ann Freas and Karen Lynn Dinkler for all the joy and inspiration the have brought into my life.

"You always wanted me to write something so, here it is."

Complete Guide To Outboard Engines, By John Fleming

INTRODUCTION

The outboard engine gets its name from the fact that it is mounted "Outboard" on the transom of the boat. On some vessels there may be extended "brackets" for mounting the engine. Certain extended brackets may be able to raise or lower the engine. They are called "jacking plates."

The outboard engine can be anything from mild to wild. It can troll at one mile per hour and five hundred RPM. It can run over 150 miles per hour and on occasion, I have seen them turn in excess of 15,000 RPM. The choices of type and purpose for which the engine is used are strictly up to you.

The fisherman can travel in a silence that permits deep meditation and the racer can run at speeds that raise the hairs on your neck, all with a two-stroke engine. A six cylinder, two-stroke engine, turning 9,500 RPM, produces 57,000 explosions per minute.

The sound is like all the little hounds from hell, turned loose at once. The speed of a hydroplane is intoxicating like a fine wine, but it is dangerous, and it is expensive. In this book we will tell you about all of them, the fast and the not so fast.

Of course, the outboard mounted engine may have a two-stroke or a four-stroke power head. In fact, the lower units or gear cases are essentially the same for either engine. The mounting brackets and tilt/trim units are, for the most part, identical. The midsection and the power heads for the two-strokes are different.

It is an understanding of the two-stroke cycle mystique which prompts this book, however, and to that end we will pursue two-stroke technology. The two-stroke power head is in a state of flux. Some say it is on the way out, but do not write it off just yet.

At a recent test site where we were testing pontoon and deck boats an engineer from Mercury Marine suggested that a "possible alternative" to the four-stroke engine was suggested by the new clean burn outboards using Opti-Max technology.

His point, and one well taken, was that it is easier to pursue one type of power head and one technology than to try to develop engines in two separate styles. It is also cheaper. This approach seems sound and practical if the EPA requirements can be met. Mercury engineers have a way of making the difficult seem entirely plausible.

Pollution laws certainly do not favor the two-stroke as it has been configured in the past, for it has been an inherently dirty engine. Direct Fuel Injection (DFI) may well clean up and extend the life of the two-stroke engine. Other technologies, only hinted at by the manufacturers, may give it life anew.

The lack of any practical four-stroke power heads in the upper horsepower classes (engines of 150 horsepower and above), makes that two-stroke a necessary commodity. High cost and excessive weight on existing engines has further conspired to delay the invasion of the four-stroke outboard. Before they totally displace the two-stroke engine they have much to prove.

Regardless of what may be contained in the final chapter of the two-stroke story, I for one shall never forget the engine. It is almost as much a part of me as an arm or leg and it has provided me with memories that I will take to the grave.

It was on the Tensaw River of Alabama that I first ran a 5 horsepower, 4 cylinder, opposed piston, Evinrude outboard engine that belonged to my father. There were so many fish then that no one can describe the situation. You would just have to be there.

I spent many quiet hours on that river and then one day I climbed into my first hydroplane. It was a Fillinger "D" boat. I took one look at that rooster tail and I was forever hooked. I still love the sound of a high-winding engine when it is running right at the edge of the possible.

Stay with me and I will tell you all about two-strokes, how they run, why they run, and why sometimes they do not run. One chapter and a few references to four-stroke outboards will be made in this book but they will only be for comparison purposes.

A good reference to four-stroke theory and operation, is the book, *Complete Guide To Marine Gasoline Engines*, published by Bristol Fashion Publications, P. O. Box 20, Enola Pennsylvania, 17025-0020, 800-478-7147.

John Fleming

TABLE OF CONTENTS

INTRODUCTION   Page 9

CHAPTER ONE   Page 17
    TWO-STROKE/FOUR-STROKE COMPARISON

CHAPTER TWO   Page 23
    WHAT DOES THE ENGINE DO?

CHAPTER THREE   Page 29
    CYLINDER BLOCK & CYLINDER HEAD

CHAPTER FOUR   Page 35
    ROTATING ASSEMBLY

CHAPTER FIVE   Page 39
    RECIPROCATING ASSEMBLY

CHAPTER SIX   Page 45
    HOW TO BALANCE THE ENGINE

CHAPTER SEVEN   Page 51
    IGNITION SYSTEMS

CHAPTER EIGHT   Page 59
    THE CARBURETOR

CHAPTER NINE   Page 65
    FUEL INJECTION

CHAPTER TEN   Page 73
TWO-STROKE VALVES

CHAPTER ELEVEN   Page 81
LUBRICATING SYSTEMS

CHAPTER TWELVE   Page 87
EXHAUST SYSTEM

CHAPTER THIRTEEN   Page 93
HOW THE ENGINE RUNS

CHAPTER FOURTEEN   Page 101
FLAME PROPAGATION

CHAPTER FIFTEEN   Page 109
MECHANICS OF TWO-STROKE ENGINES

CHAPTER SIXTEEN   Page 117
ENGINE DESIGN

CHAPTER SEVENTEEN   Page 123
PAN, COWL & DRIVE SHAFT HOUSING

CHAPTER EIGHTEEN   Page 131
THE GEAR CASE

CHAPTER NINETEEN   Page 139
PROPELLERS

CHAPTER TWENTY   Page 147
SETUP THE ENGINE

CHAPTER TWENTY-ONE   Page 155
A MEASURE OF EFFICIENCY & PERFORMANCE

CHAPTER TWENTY-TWO   Page 165
TROUBLESHOOTING

CHAPTER TWENTY-THREE   Page 171
A BIT OF HISTORY

ABOUT THE AUTHOR   Page 187

CHAPTER ONE

TWO-STROKE FOUR-STROKE COMPARISON

I want to remove a few myths before we get into the subject of two-stroke outboards. How do they really compare to their four-stroke brethren? Comparisons come in seven important areas: physical size, weight, cost, fuel consumption, noise, pollution, and comparative power.

First, let us consider physical size. Horsepower for horsepower, the carbureted two-stroke engine is generally much smaller than a four-stroke of comparable horsepower. The fuel injected, two-strokes however require additional accessories to make the injection systems work. They are closer in both size and weight to a four-stroke engine of comparable horsepower.

Two-stroke engines with ratings of 25 horsepower and below still have carburetors and they are much smaller than their four-stroke counterparts. The size of the small horsepower four-strokes is causing their owners some problems in small spaces such as outboard auxiliary applications where the engine is in a well.

How about weight? The weight comparisons between two-stroke engines and four-stroke engines will vary from horsepower rating to horsepower rating and by year of manufacture. In some instances the four-stroke engine will be only a tiny bit heavier. In others, the difference will be dramatic. There are niche engines where the two styles are almost equal in weight.

Perhaps the greatest contrast still apparent today lies in the areas of small horsepower engines and very large horsepower engines. In these two areas alone, the two-stroke is dramatically lighter than the four-stroke. Among offshore fishermen and those who need to power dinghies or canoes, the carbureted two-strokes are revered for their smaller size and lighter weight.

Engines in the 2 horsepower to 15 horsepower range are generally considered portable when manufactured as two-stroke engines. As a four-stroke engine they no longer are. Four-stroke engines in the 8 horsepower range are about as heavy as you can carry.

A 5 horsepower, two-stroke engine is about 35 percent lighter than a 5 horsepower four-stroke but this weight advantage does not extend to all comparisons between the two engine types. How about one of those niches where the comparison is closer? Try the Mercury 115 horsepower and 135 horsepower V-6 engines with OptiMax injection.

Here the manufacturer has de-rated a high horsepower engine, the standard 150, to keep down cost of construction for a smaller horsepower unit. I refer to these de-rated engines as hybrids. In manufacturing the hybrid engines, Mercury has built a pair of units which very nearly equal a comparable horsepower four-stroke in weight.

How close are they? The 115 horsepower, two-stroke, Mercury engine, built on a V-6 block and employing the Opti-Max fuel injection system weighs well over 400 pounds. This is only a bit less than the four-stroke, 115 horsepower, Honda engine. In fact, it is actually heavier than the 2000 model Yamaha F-115 four-stroke.

The introduction of the light Yamaha four-stroke, F-115 constitutes the first time (to my knowledge) a four-stroke has been lighter than a two-stroke, at any horsepower rating. The high horsepower-to-weight ratio of those hybrid two-strokes limits their use just as similar constraints limit the Honda four-stroke.

While this is the only example I can cite in which a two-stroke engine outweighs a four-stroke of comparable horsepower, it is not the only case where the weights are close. The 135 horsepower, V-6 Mercury with OptiMax fuel injection weighs only a few pounds less than the 130 horsepower Honda four-stroke. Like the 115 horsepower V-6 in the above example, the 135 horsepower V-6 Mercury engine is also built on the same block. Both are hybrids to the V-6 150 horsepower engine.

Remember these are extreme cases and I cite them only to demonstrate the fact that the weight consideration generally favors the two-stroke engine by a wide margin.

There is another niche to be considered. It is in horsepower ratings above 130 that the two-stroke really starts to pull away. Again, because of certain inherent design characteristics, the two-stroke can stretch the horsepower available from a 480 to 500 pound, V-6 block to much higher levels, with no increase in weight.

The four-stroke has no such potential. The largest two-stroke engine in use today is a 300 horsepower atom smasher from Mercury Marine. This engine weighs about 500 pounds. There is only a small difference in weight between the 130 horsepower, Honda four-stroke engine and the 300 horsepower two-stroke.

This is really a terrible disparity with that 300 horsepower two-stroke producing more than twice the horsepower for the same weight. As they are designed today, the four-stroke has no potential to bridge the gap.

Cost is a very real consideration in this market. Forget the list prices of any engine and concentrate on what you really pay for the delivered unit. Four-stroke engines are much more costly than a matching two-stroke engine. Generally, about 35 percent to 50 percent higher.

Fuel economy. The four-stroke engine is very economical to operate in the low to midrange speeds. At full throttle it is just as thirsty as an average two-stroke. There are many ways to compare engines but you will see the best methods in the chapter on "Efficiency." Any advantage the four-stroke may have in economy of operation will still take many years to recoup the difference in cost.

Smoke and pollution. Make the comparison in three areas. Compare any carbureted two-stoke engine to a four-stroke of like horsepower and the four-stroke is the unquestioned winner. Add EFI (Electronic Fuel Injection) to the mix and the two-stroke improves just a bit but the four-stroke still wins, going away.

The newer DFI (Direct Fuel Injected) two-strokes are different. They rival the four-stroke in several different categories within which they were unable to compete previously; fuel economy is one of those categories.

Noise. The answers are much the same. In the two-stroke category, only the latest DFI engines can equal a four-stroke for sound deadening. The exception to this is top speed operation. At top speed there seems to be little difference in the sound level of the various outboard engines. For reasons which have to do with resonance and other factors, the four-stroke engine gains considerable sound at top RPM.

That leaves the question of pollution and here the four-stroke is the natural leader. Again, the differences are becoming smaller every year as two-stroke, DFI engines are developed to their full potential.

The two-stroke engine can match the existing standards for emissions and probably those in the future. It is difficult for me to believe that the four-cycle engine will fail to be the pollution control champ, if by only a small margin.

Horsepower. The largest four-stroke outboard engine on the market today comes from Honda Marine. It develops only 130 horsepower and weighs close to 500 pounds. This is as much weight as you can bolt onto the transom of a boat. By today's standards, this is not a lot of horsepower.

Two of these monsters weigh half a ton. This limits the user of the four-stroke to certain sizes and styles of vessel, or it poses a restriction on available speed. The total of 260 horsepower available from both engines dictates the potential applications. Twin 130's are not likely to make 60 miles per hour on a center console fisherman.

The largest two-stroke, V-6 engine from Mercury Marine also weighs about 500 pounds but it develops 300 horsepower. More horsepower than two of those largest four-strokes for the same weight as one.

Engines of the past. In 1997 a 200 horsepower, 2.5 liter, V-6 Mercury engine weighed 385 pounds. Today a Mercury 200 horsepower engine with OptiMax fuel injection weighs very close to 500 pounds: a 34 percent increase in weight. From this comparison it is easy to see the engines are going in opposite directions. The two-stroke gets heavier while the four-stroke is approaching parity.

Four-stroke outboard's claim to be a stronger engine, horsepower for horsepower. That claim is unfounded. If we compare two engines, one a two-stroke and the other a four-stroke, each rated at 100 horsepower, they will each produce 100 horsepower.

If either engine produces more than 100 horsepower it should have a different rating. One horsepower will do the same amount of work by whatever manner it is produced.

Of course, they are still two totally different concepts in terms of engine type and operation.

The reason the two-stroke engine is able to produce higher horsepower outputs at the same weight as the smaller horsepower four-strokes will be explained in later pages. In a word, the difference lies in the tuning of a two-stroke engine and in this instance, tuning does not mean what you think.

Rather than the process of adjustment we think of as "tuning" in the classic sense, power tuning for the two-stroke engine involves the intake, exhaust systems, carburetors and reed valves. By judicious manipulation of the sizes and dimensions of these components we are able to get a wide variety of horsepower levels from the same cylinder block.

Thus the same basic components such as crankshaft, pistons, rods, and other expensive parts need not be changed from horsepower rating to horsepower rating. This saves a manufacturer substantial construction costs. It also saves you money.

You are about to enter the world of two-stroke where your imagination is the only real limit. Engines that develop 5.2 horsepower per cubic inch, naturally aspirated, have already run their way into the record books.

This is not a hot rod manual. We will thoroughly detail the everyday outboard and its operation. For the big two-stroke engines, that everyday performance is beyond the potential of any present four-stroke outboard.

The bone stock, 1988 model, 70 horsepower Johnson engine actually developed about 75 horsepower. It got that horsepower from just 49 cubic inches and that is about 1.5 horsepower for every one of those cubic inches. If we asked a 350-cubic-inch inboard engine to do this same job it would have to make 575 horsepower in its stock form. Today that 350-cubic-inch inboard engine produces slightly more than 285 horsepower.

Even a mild two-stroke engine is an exciting piece of work. It has capabilities and assets not found on any other type of engine. Consider the facts. The 1997 model, 200 horsepower Mercury engine I mentioned before weighed just 1.9 pounds per horsepower and remember, that includes the transmission.

In time, the two-stroke may go the way of the dinosaur but while they live, you have got to love 'em.

CHAPTER TWO

WHAT DOES THE ENGINE DO?

The two stroke outboard takes a chemical fuel and converts it to heat energy. This conversion is made by the process of combustion (burning). The engine must then convert that heat energy to usable power. To accomplish this the engine needs two types of motion: reciprocating motion and rotary motion.

Reciprocating motion is up and down or back and forth motion which we get from a piston as it moves in the cylinder bores. Expanding gasses from the burning fuel create a pressure in the cylinder. The piston is the only thing that can move and this cylinder pressure causes it to do so. This is our reciprocating motion (up and down.)

The crankshaft converts this reciprocating motion into rotary motion (round and round) which is the most usable form of power for our purposes. Heat energy is now available as usable power. This is the short description of what an engine does.

Of course, this is an oversimplification but, stated in a few words, it is quite accurate and complete. How the engine accomplishes these things is another story and a rather fascinating one at that. I will describe the two-stroke cycle and how it works. Then we will approach the matter of parts, pieces, and engine construction. The two-stroke cycle is not easily described so please read carefully.

Every piston engine makes two strokes for each 360 degree revolution of the crankshaft, one up and the other down. The two-stroke engine is often described as a 360-degree engine because it fires on each revolution.

Each time the engine rotates, or after each of the two-strokes, if you prefer, this engine will fire. The name two-stroke engine is accurate, to a degree. Another often applied label, two-cycle is not entirely accurate. In fact, the engine must go through five cycles or events during each group of two strokes.

Four of those cycles you are probably familiar with but the fifth cycle is little understood. Keep in mind all five of these cycles do occur in a single revolution. The five cycles are Intake, Compression, Power and Exhaust/Transfer.

The intake and compression cycles occur on the same stroke. The power and exhaust cycles occur on the succeeding stroke. The transfer cycle occurs during the exhaust stroke. Later in this book we will run the engine and put this process into motion. For now, it is sufficient to know why the engine is called a two-stroke.

It is necessary to identify the several parts and establish a name for each, so you know what is being discussed. We will approach the descriptive process first. Next, I will put those pieces into assemblies and systems. Then we will set the entire thing in motion and see how it works. It is important to identify these parts in a common manner in order to understand technical discussions.

The engine may employ a carburetor or an injector to provide fuel to the engine. The air/fuel mix for a two-stroke engine is inducted through the crankcase of the engine and thus it has a totally different type of intake manifold from that of a four-stroke engine. There is not a true, separately cast, manifold, as with the four-stroke engine.

The valve arrangements of a two-stroke are also unique. The valves may be reed valves, piston port valves, sleeve valves or rotary valves. There are in fact two types of rotary valves: internal rotary valves and external rotary valves. Each of these is different but all are in use today.

The cylinder block for a two-stroke may be for a one, two, three, four, six, or eight cylinder engine. These cylinders may be in line or in a V configuration. Different companies use varying degrees of separation in the V shape of the cylinders.

The 90 degree V was common for many years but both the 60 degree V and the 76 degree V are in use today. There was an older model Mercury engine that employed a 15 degree V bank. Certain models of Evinrude outboard engines from the '30s and '40s had opposed pistons in a flat configuration.

The opposed piston engine had pistons facing away from the crankshaft and opposite to each other. They moved directly towards or away from their opposing partners and this provided an inherently balanced condition. If the opposed piston engine has static balance (at rest) it also has dynamic balance (in motion).

A very successful German racing engine was manufactured by Dieter Koenig. The engine bore Koenig's name and it had opposed pistons. That engine was very fast, very dependable and is still competitive in A. P. B. A. races today. Opposed piston engines are seldom seen anymore but they have been quite popular.

The cylinder head for the two-stroke is a very simple cover for the cylinder. It has water passages for cooling and a combustion chamber milled or cast into the inside. The spark plugs are threaded into the cylinder head and are exposed to the combustion chamber.

Pistons for the two-stroke may be flat tops or deflector heads depending upon the type of engine involved. As this theme develops, we will detail the like qualities, as well as, the differences between the loop charged engine and the cross port engine for which these different types of pistons are designed.

The two-stroke engine uses a piston to transmit pressure from burning gasses and piston rings to seal that pressure within the cylinder. These are compression rings only. There are no oil control rings on a two-stroke piston since there is no oil in the crankcase to control. Oil is mixed with the gasoline or provided by a pump from a remote supply.

There are generally two compression rings on the two-stroke piston. In a few of the older engines there were three. It was decided this was unnecessary drag and two rings would seal adequately. In a few racing engines, there is only one. This is done in an effort to keep friction to a minimum. There is no expectation of longevity and an engine that runs ten minutes in this severe racing service is a good one.

The engine employs a connecting rod which connects the piston to the crankshaft. The connecting rod has a wrist pin which connects the little end of the connecting rod to the piston. This portion of the rod moves up and down with the piston.

The big end of the connecting rod circles the crankshaft with bearings to reduce friction. This big end of the connecting rod transmits energy from the piston to the crank arm and it turns around with the crankshaft. The connecting rod may employ a cracked cap or a full circle at the big end. The choice is dictated by the design of the crankshaft.

There are two styles of crankshafts used on two-stroke engines. There is a one piece crankshaft and a full circle crankshaft to choose from. Some manufacturers swear by one piece crankshafts and others tout the full circle unit. We will detail the differences in chapter four.

Whichever style is used in the engine they share these common characteristics. All crankshafts have an arm and counterweights cast or forged into their bodies. The crankshaft employs pins or journals to carry the big end of the connecting rod. It has machined surfaces for the crankcase seals and the main bearings.

The crankshaft has another machined surface that is both tapered and keyed to accept the flywheel. The tapered section of the crankshaft centers or aligns the flywheel while the key way keeps it from slipping as crankshaft speeds vary rapidly. Inertia in the flywheel exerts considerable force against the crankshaft and this is an important joining.

The flywheel is seldom a simple weight on the two-stroke as it is on the four-stroke. It will generally have various magnets affixed to the inside perimeter. They have a specific location in relation to the crankshaft position. The key between the crankshaft and the flywheel maintains this position. We will explore the purpose of these magnets as the book continues.

A reed cage with reed valves may appear on the engine or it may employ a rotary valve with a rotor. The piston port engine uses the piston itself plus the ports for valving. All of these systems use a silencer on the intake to help quiet the engine.

The two-stroke engine may use a magneto for ignition and that magneto may be incorporated into the flywheel or it may be a separate, belt driven accessory. Engines built in the last 15 years will universally employ the more modern systems. The Capacitive Discharge (CD) or High Energy Ignition (HEI) ignition systems are preferred by most manufacturers.

Virtually all of these systems are located beneath the flywheel. All are in some way controlled or influenced by a spark or impulse generated by various mechanisms located under that whirling piece of metal.

The two-stroke engine may have an electrically driven starter and is referred to as an electric start engine. It may employ only a manual starter which means you pull on a rope or cord to start the engine. There are few self-winding engines around now, but in bygone times, you had to wind the starter cord onto the flywheel, put both feet against the engine and pull. With luck, the engine didn't pull back.

The engine may have a power tilt and trim or you may have to raise and lower the engine manually. The many uses for the PT/T will be detailed in Chapter 17. The power tilt and trim system uses hydraulic cylinders and a motor to accomplish its purpose. Switches to activate this system are located on the throttle handle and the engine cowling.

The lower unit or gear case appears at the base of the midsection or drive shaft housing. It is in effect a reduction gear and clutch. On some racing engines this gear case is very streamlined. The gearing is 1:1, there is no reduction, and the drive is direct. No shifting is possible.

The alternator for an outboard engine may be mounted on the side of the block and driven with a belt. More often they are located beneath the flywheel and employ magnets and coils which are mounted there. These alternators are quite compact and surprisingly trouble free.

Beneath the flywheel is a stator on which all these parts are mounted. On some engines the stator moves with the throttle advance or retard and changes the spark timing. Others use an Electronic Control Module (ECM) which accomplishes this purpose, automatically, in response to a throttle position sensor.

On many of the engines built since 1979 there is an oil tank and a pump which provides lubricating oil to the engine. These pumps vary the ratio of oil to fuel and they may have a tank on the engine beneath the cowling, or they may use a separate, remote reservoir.

These are the major parts of an outboard engine. In the following chapters I will describe each of these parts in detail and discuss their purpose. As this book progresses, I will put the parts together and make them run. For the next chapter I will begin the descriptions with the cylinder block.

CHAPTER THREE

THE CYLINDER BLOCK & CYLINDER HEAD

Almost the entire two-stroke outboard engine is manufactured of aluminum. This includes the cylinder block, cylinder head, and other major external parts. The casting process for the aluminum block is called Lost Foam Casting and this is a marvelous achievement unto itself.

The lost foam process can produce relatively precise reproductions of tortuous and convoluted shapes. It has helped to keep the weight down on the outboard engine by making it possible to use thinner castings for any part or piece. This thinner casting is possible because there are fewer flaws.

The process begins with a foam mold which has exactly the shape the foundry wishes to reproduce. The foam mold is placed in an iron core box. The core box is filled with a casting sand that fills every crack and crevice of the foam mold. The foam mold is positioned by this sand and by the limits of the core box.

When the hot metal enters the core box the foam is lost or melted away and replaced by molten metal. You now have a perfect casting with dimensions closely controlled. The process is relatively cheap since foam molds costs little to mass produce. There are few castings of this type lost due to flaws or errors.

Because it is made of aluminum, the outboard engine is

subject to a kind of controlled destruction process, if it is used in saltwater. The salt corrodes the engine and, little by little, it will surely destroy it. Only high tech alloys with special coatings allow it to survive. The aluminum alloys used in the outboard engine contain certain amounts of copper.

The special coatings used on the outer surfaces are baked on and consist of numerous layers. They vary from manufacturer to manufacturer. They have catchy names and their composition is a closely guarded secret. There is an entire chapter on corrosion and paint processes later in the book.

Worse than corrosion is electrolysis which occurs when two dissimilar metals are present in an electrolyte. All the fastenings on external parts of the two-stroke are made of stainless steel. Aluminum does not have the tensile strength to be used for nuts or bolts. Since the fastenings cannot be aluminum, they must be a dissimilar metal and this requirement provides the second or unlike metal that can cause electrolysis.

As we have seen above, aluminum construction does pose problems. Yet, it helps to keep the overall weight of the engine to a minimum. Light weight is an important part of why the two-stroke engine first came into being. Without it, much of the charm in two-stroke engines would be lost.

The cylinder block and cylinder head for many four-stroke outboard engines are made of cast iron and copied from an automobile. In fact, more than half of those larger four-stroke outboard engines have such an origin. The weight of those iron castings account for the weight problems the four-stroke encounters.

The cylinder block and upper half of the crankcase for a two-stroke engine are cast and machined as a single unit. The lower half of the crankcase is cast separately but it is machined as a mated part for the block.

The cylinder block and lower crankcase half must also have sealing circles or sealing rings machined into their inner surfaces. There must be one sealing device for each cylinder. The cylinders on a two-stroke must be isolated from each other. The reason for this is the transfer cycle which requires crankcase compression. For this stage of our discussion, it is sufficient to realize that provisions are made in the block and crankcase castings to isolate the cylinders.

The two-stroke engine does not have a common intake manifold to serve all cylinders. There is no potential to utilize one. As we progress you will realize a multicylinder, two-stroke engine is a series of single cylinder power plants working in harmony.

Figure 1

Main bearings.

The main bearings and the seal rings are supported in the machined surfaces between the two halves of the crankcase. The bolts which hold the two castings together are relatively heavy since the lower half of the crankcase serves as the main bearing caps. It will carry much of the load from the crankshaft.

The two-cycle cylinder block has scantlings cast into its body for bracing and strength. It has webbing at certain stress points, such as the main bearings, to brace and strengthen the bearing supports. The cylinder block is subject to a certain amount of flexing as the pressure of combustion is applied.

There is a series of ports machined into the block that penetrate the cylinder walls. These inlet and exhaust ports replace the conventional valves used on a four-stroke engine.

A transfer passage from the crankcase to the cylinder carries air/fuel mix to the intake ports.

The cylinder block employs a sleeve or steel insert in the bores to reduce wear between the piston, rings, and cylinders. This sleeve has ports milled through its walls, as does the block itself. The sleeve then is not easily replaced if it should be damaged. First, it has a very tight fit to hold it in place. Second, it must be placed exactly, so the ports align properly. If the sleeve should be misaligned the intake and exhaust ports would be partially blocked and restrict the breathing of the engine.

There are two types of porting systems in use on two-stroke engines. They are referred to as cross port cylinders and loop charged cylinders. The porting arrangement is vastly different between the two and some of the internal parts are different also. For this reason, each will be treated separately when we start to run the engine.

Many two-stroke engines use a set of freestanding cylinders which have no deck or common webbing at the top of the block. This helps deaden sound because the sonic wave is contained in the standing cylinder and not transferred to the outer walls.

These types of cylinders do actually vibrate and flex within themselves. They have a tendency to release the head gasket and allow the incursion of water into the cylinder bores. For this reason they were abandoned some years ago. They did exist for two decades however and served better than one would expect.

There are two alternative sealing arrangements for the cylinder head. The first of these is the no-gasket cylinder head which is in use today. This system employs a closely machined surface for both cylinder head and cylinder block. There is no gasket as we saw in the earlier engines.

A neoprene sealing ring is installed into two mated grooves. The grooves are machined into the surfaces of cylinder head and cylinder block alike. A sealing mastic is coated onto the surfaces, at assembly. The combination of sealing mastic and closely machined surfaces is relied upon to contain the heat and pressure of combustion. The neoprene sealing ring is for water control.

This system varies markedly from the conventional four-stroke engine because by lacking a cylinder head gasket. The earliest of these gasketless heads tended to leak a bit with time but the type and placement of the bolts was perfected and today there are very few failures.

The last type of cylinder arrangement has the cylinder head cast integral with the cylinder block and it is not removable. Pistons for this type of engine must be stuffed into the cylinder from the bottom of the crankcase.

There are special ring compressors for this purpose but some older mechanics prefer to fish the rings in with their fingers.

I know of only one four-stroke engine that employed this principal and that was an old Crosley automobile engine. The valves were still located in that one piece cylinder head and trying to grind them was a chore. A special tool with a very long mandrel did the job, but it was a trying experience.

Water passages in the cylinder block are open around all sides of the cylinders and there are a limited number of oil transfer ports or openings drilled into the crankcase. These oil passages serve a different function from those on a four-stroke and we will detail this function later.

Bolt holes in the machined surfaces allow the placement of cap screws into the cylinder block. They accept the bolts which retain the cylinder heads, port covers and reed valve system. There are other threaded holes which accommodate accessories and the exhaust housing.

The cylinder head itself is a simple cover for the cylinder. It has no intake or exhaust valves but it may have a compression release valve installed. This valve is present on manual start outboard engines only. It is activated by a cam and lever set from the self starter.

When the starter rope is pulled, the lever actuates the compression release valve and a portion of the cylinder pressure is bled off to allow easier starting. This greatly reduces the effort needed to pull the starter cord.

There is a threaded spark plug hole in the cylinder head and a combustion chamber machined into it on the side towards the cylinder. This combustion chamber is very important and it is most carefully shaped. The cross-port engine and the loop-charged engine each possess a distinctive shape.

The shape and size of the combustion chamber on each of these systems does control the compression ratio and effects the flame propagation in their cylinders. Thus, the combustion chamber shapes, though different, serve essentially the same function for these two different engines.

The mounting for the stator is bolted to the top of the cylinder block and any other accessories such as a self starter or external alternator are also mounted to this casting. The cylinder block on the two-stroke resembles most other engines in that it is the skeleton on which the entire engine rests.

The two-stroke engine has no lubricating oil pump in the crankcase, therefore it has no need for an oil gallery, it has no camshaft or lifters. The cylinder head is a much simpler device since it has no port runners, valves, valve springs, or rocker arms.

In fact, the two-stroke, as a whole, has fewer moving parts and that also contributes to the lower weight. This is a simple engine. Only the electronics are likely to get a bit sticky from time to time.

CHAPTER FOUR

ROTATING ASSEMBLY

I am going to separate the major moving parts of the engine into two groups. The rotating assembly consists of those parts which turn while the reciprocating assembly consists of parts which move up and down.

This chapter will be dedicated to the rotating assembly while Chapter Five will explore the reciprocating assembly. They are interdependent but separate entities, and they operate on different rules.

The rotating mass or rotating assembly includes the crankshaft, the flywheel, the big end of the connecting rod, connecting rod bearings, and bearing retainers at the big end. All of these parts are balanced together.

Let us consider each of the rotating parts, beginning with the crankshaft. The crankshaft for a two-stroke engine is always made of steel, and portions of the shaft require different qualities. The two main qualities are toughness and hardness.

Toughness is the ability to maintain a shape, under load, while hardness is the ability to resist surface deformation.

Chrome molly steel is the metal most often used in the two-stroke crankshaft. It is selected because it is inherently tough and hard but the manufacturer uses certain processes to enhance both of these qualities. These processes are forging and induction hardening. Each of these processes is very effective to achieve its desired purpose.

Added toughness is usually achieved by the forging

process. Forging aligns the surface molecules from end to end. It also binds the surface molecules together and tends to toughen the entire shaft. Forging is a process that employs some type of impact.

Chrome molly can be hardened by a different process called induction hardening and portions of the crankshaft are hardened in that manner. Very high temperatures and controlled cooling processes produce this hardening that is so important to the two-cycle crankshaft.

An induction furnace provides both the heat and the controlled cooling necessary for surface hardening. Hardness is difficult to obtain without brittleness and thus it is desirable only on very restricted portions of the crankshaft. The only surfaces to be hardened are those on which the bearings ride.

The system for controlling the hardening process employs a shield that protects broad areas of the crankshaft from the effects of hardening. This shield is made of a copper alloy which is plated onto these parts of the crankshaft. It appears as a kind of bronze or copper color over the shiny steel surface.

If you pick up a two-stroke crankshaft you can see this coloration on those affected parts and see the brighter colors of the machined and hardened crankshaft journals which were not coated. The hardened areas are needed because the two-stroke crankshaft uses roller bearings on the big ends of the connecting rods and on some areas for main bearings.

From the earliest outboard engines, to the 1980s it was considered impossible to rebuild a crankshaft for a two-stroke engine. Many efforts were made to do so but effective welding and heat treating processes plus the surface hardening of the journals simply evaded the machinist and rebuilder. Good, dependable, rebuilt crankshafts for two-stroke engines began to appear from several sources in the late 1980s. Today they are fairly common and a number of rebuilders do excellent work in this field.

We have explored most of the common attributes that are shared by all two-stroke crankshafts. Now let us consider the two separate types, one piece crankshafts and full circle crankshafts.

I will begin with the one piece crankshaft. This unit employs cracked cap connecting rods which actually have a removable, bolt-on, cap. This cap is removed during assembly and a set of needle roller bearings are installed between the cap and the crankshaft. These bearings may be loose or caged.

The loose style bearings are held in place with a firm grease during assembly. The caged bearing has retainers of metal or plastic into which the roller bearings are inserted. The cap is then replaced on the connecting rod and the bolts installed. This completes the connecting rod installation.

Figure 2

Crankshaft.

The full circle crankshaft is another matter. This unit has a series of forgings which resemble dinner plates. There is a machined hole in each of the plates which accept a pressed-in pin for the connecting rods to ride upon. Both the roller bearings and a crank pin are inserted in the big end of the full circle, capless, connecting rod.

The two cheek pieces are then pressed together, onto each end of the crankpin, with a force measured in excess of one hundred fifty thousand pounds. The full circle connecting rod has no bolts to fail nor cap to come loose. On the other hand, the one piece crankshaft has no pressed-in pins to fail. Manufacturers of each will naturally claim superiority but I see little difference in performance. The two-stroke crankshaft is very reliable, regardless of type.

Two-stroke engines tend to be high RPM engines and not torquers. The developed torque is modest and the crankshaft arm is short, giving a comparatively short stroke. The crankshaft must be tough to hold its shape because it is a very small casting for the horsepower it develops.

It must be very hard in spots because the surface of the crankshaft is actually the inner race for the roller bearings of the connecting rods and main bearings run. The connecting rods themselves are the outer race for this bearing system and hard inserts are molded into the crankcase halves to support the main rollers.

These roller bearings are referred to as anti-friction bearings. This is not an exactly accurate description since all bearings exert some friction on the surfaces they protect but the roller bearing does generate less friction than a bushing. The roller bearings truly do reduce the rolling friction in the engine, but they demand much of the crankshaft itself in return.

A roller bearing is meant to run on zero lash, which implies a perfect fit but there is always a certain amount of clearance. The loose needles create both a particular sound and a particular vibration of their own. This bearing does not give as much support to the crankshaft as a bushing might so there are some tradeoffs.

This is the two-cycle, highly developed, crankshaft. If possible, try to see one at a local outboard shop. Hold it in your hands and see the features which we have described.

CHAPTER FIVE

RECIPROCATING ASSEMBLY

All of the parts in the reciprocating assembly move up and down or back and forth. They consist of the piston, piston rings, wrist pin, wrist pin locks, small end of the connecting rod and wrist pin bearing. The small end of the connecting rod moves with the piston.

Mass or weight which rotates like the crankshaft can be balanced. Weight which reciprocates cannot be balanced but must rather be counterbalanced. Chapter Six will deal with the subject of balance and related occurrences.

The piston has a crown, or top to accept the pressure from burning gasses. It has a skirt or sides to accept the thrust loads placed upon it. The shape of the crown varies from engine type to engine type. The skirts may or may not have ports let into their sides. The piston for the two-stroke engine may be flat on top or it may be domed.

There are two principle styles of two-stroke engines in use today. The loop-charged engine is most prevalent in the modern era. The cross-port engine was once the rage and it is still around to some extent.

Loop-charged engines use flat-topped pistons while cross-port engines use deflector head pistons. The dome on a deflector-head piston has a special shape to deflect the incoming gas/air mix upward, into the combustion chamber.

The loop charged engine depends upon the opposing forces of gasses coming from opposite sides of the cylinder to retain them within that cylinder. The single exhaust port is on a third side away from the loop of fresh charge.

Below the piston top, the two pistons are much alike. They have a series of lands and grooves machined into their sides to accept the piston rings. The tops of these areas are described as lands while the rings ride inside the grooves.

The fit between the piston rings and the grooves is important and the grooves are machined to close tolerances. A dowel pin is pressed into the bottom of the ring groove and rises half way to the top of the groove. The dowel pin aligns with a slot in the ends of the piston rings and retains the rings in a set position. This dowel pin prevents the ring gap from aligning itself over a port opening and possibly destroying the rings.

Piston rings in the two-stroke engine are continuously faced with the problem of passing across the open jaws of the inlet and exhaust ports in the cylinder bores. If the rings fit too tightly in the bores or expansion from heat puts too much pressure on the end gaps, the rings will migrate into the ports and be broken off.

This is one occurrence which will destroy an engine. Ring fit and alignment are critical to longevity on any two-stroke engine. They are more important on late model engines where ports are both large and numerous.

The piston has a taper from crown to skirt, or top to bottom, if you prefer. It is narrower at the top and has a greater clearance between itself and the cylinder wall. This because the greater heat which is applied to the crown will cause more expansion at that point.

During operation the crown will expand more rapidly than the skirt until, at operating temperature, the piston is nearly straight. Because of this initial shape, the piston is said to be tapered.

There have been a few piston port engines manufactured in the past. These engines used only those ports machined into the piston skirt to replace any other type of valve in the engine. The loop charged engine also employs passages machined into the piston skirt but it utilizes reed valves for sealing. The operation of each of these systems will be detailed in Chapter 13.

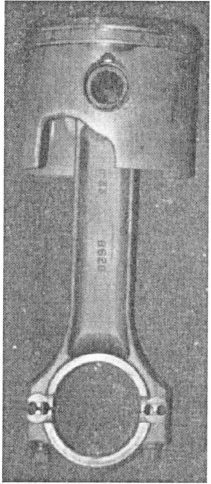

Figure 3

This illustrates all the components in the piston and rod assembly.

The piston has a wrist pin boss which is a thickening of the skirt where the wrist pin bore is located. The wrist pin fits into this bore and is supported by the webbing in the piston. There is a great amount of stress applied to this point during combustion. The piston tends to expand more at that point on the piston because of the greater thickness. Thus the piston may be cam ground or egg shaped at this juncture. It may only be relieved by some type of machined indenture but it will surely have an allowance for the added expansion at the wrist pin boss.

The wrist pin itself is made of very tough steel and hardened on its surface. The wrist pin serves as another inner race for a roller bearing. The wrist pin bearing may be a caged type or a set of loose bearings. If it is caged, the roller bearing itself is pressed into the small end of the connecting rod. If the bearings are loose rollers, they are stuck into the small end of the connecting rod and held in place with a firm grease, during assembly. In either case, the wrist pin is inserted into the roller bearings as it passes, side to side, through the wrist pin boss.

In the instance of the caged rollers the bearing cage is the outer race or working surface for the rollers and the wrist pin is the inner race. For the loose roller bearings, the inner surface of the small end of the connecting rod is the outer race, while the wrist pin is the inner race.

The wrist pin is retained inside the piston with a set of pin locks. These locks may be spiral wire inserted into a machined groove or they may be circ-clips which require a special set of pliers to remove. The wrist pin lock prevents the wrist pin from dragging on the cylinder bores and damaging their surface.

Piston rings for the two-stroke engine have been made with many exotic shapes. There have been Dykes' rings, sometimes called L rings, because of their cross sectional shape. There have been oval shaped rings which were referred to as pressure back rings and there have even been conventional shaped rings used on two stroke pistons.

These odd shapes were fostered by the twin problems of vibration and friction. The two stroke operates at high RPM and it fires every time it turns one revolution. This gives rise to special vibration problems. Early engines were provided with piston rings that employed higher ring-to-cylinder wall pressures to allow for this problem. The added tension in the rings caused increased friction and used horsepower to overcome the drag. Then came the Dykes ring which sat at the very top of the piston and ran in the fire. Visualize if you will, a piston ring that has the long side of the L towards the piston.

The pressure of the burning gasses can get between the top of the piston and the space between piston and ring. This pressure exerts added force to hold the ring against the cylinder wall and makes it possible to use less ring tension. As the ring wears, the cylinder pressure remains constant and this pressure, added to the natural ring tension, was expected to extend ring life.

In the best of all worlds, this system worked quite well but the results were sometimes less than desirable. Heat from the cylinder could grossly effect the exposed ring if the engine was overloaded. The awkward shapes machined into the piston sometimes led to groove failure which always caused cylinder damage.

The Dykes ring was a great idea for a racing engine that was to be torn down frequently but in a stock engine that had to last for many years it sometimes failed prematurely. Carbon build up could sound a death knell for this piston ring so it is seldom seen today.

The pressure back ring was a creation of OMC Corporation. This ring design employed an oval shaped ring in a matching groove with the sharp edge at the top of the oval turned to the cylinder wall. This piston ring was also pressed against the cylinder wall by compression as the piston rose.

On the down stroke the ring rotated away from the wall and pressure was reduced. Drag was also reduced accordingly. The groove for the pressure back ring was located on the side of the piston in the conventional manner. This took the ring away from the direct heat of combustion and the rotating movement of the ring in its oval groove retarded the formation of carbon deposits. The longevity of this ring was good but it did not like to overheat. That sealing lip or area at the top of the ring could get into the port area if ring expansion was sufficient.

The conventional shaped piston ring with a more or less square cross section is very much in vogue today. Newer metals with better alloys have helped. Thinner piston rings with less bearing area on the cylinder walls have helped to reduce friction.

We now believe that fewer piston rings are sufficient and two piston rings per piston are all we see today. Two-stroke racing engines may have only one piston ring for each piston. Of course, these rings are replaced after every race so they are not expected to live for any great length of time.

Regardless of the type or number of rings the piston employs, the two-stroke piston must have those dowel pins in the ring grooves. That notch on the back side of the piston ring must align with the dowel pin during the assembly process. Failure to properly align these dowel pins in the piston rings, will lead to certain ring failure, during assembly. The piston rings can even be broken while still in the ring compressor. Failing this, they will surely be broken as they enter the cylinder. The engine is then doomed from the start.

This is the reciprocating assembly. For the two-stroke engine, both the piston and the connecting rod are much different from that of the four-stroke engine. Some of the differences we have already discussed. More will become apparent as we run the engine.

CHAPTER SIX

HOW TO
BALANCE THE ENGINE

The term balance can be confusing when applied to any piston engine. The rotating mass, the weight which rotates, consists of the crankshaft, flywheel, big ends of the connecting rods, and roller bearings. This weight can be balanced unto itself.

The reciprocating mass weight which moves up and down consists of the piston, piston rings, wrist pin, wrist pin locks and roller bearing for the small end of the connecting rod. This weight can only be counterbalanced. What does this mean?

The piston is traveling in a straight line. It stops completely, twice every revolution. At top dead center and at bottom dead center there are about 5 degrees of crankshaft rotation which are described as dead travel. The crankshaft turns but the piston does not move.

This requires the piston to stop completely and start again, twice for each rotation of the crankshaft. These starts and stops are abrupt and violent. They create a great amount of vibration and the energy lost in the effort to make these stops and starts is a major source of power loss in the piston engine.

The piston-related vibrations are referred to as second harmonic vibrations. What are we to do about those vibrations? We counterbalance the weight of the reciprocating masses. The counterbalance is a device by which opposing forces counter each other. In the instance of the two-cycle crankshaft, the counterbalance is a weight cast into the crankshaft on the side opposite the connecting rod journal. It always moves counter to (in opposition to) the movement of the piston. As the piston moves upward, the counterweight rotates downward. When the piston starts down, the counterweight rotates upward. They must generate equal forces.

The counterweight must hit both dead center positions, at exactly the same time and perfectly synchronized with the piston's arrival at the opposing location. This does not cancel the force from the movement. In fact, it doubles the total energy loss and doubles the total load upon the crankshaft.

The benefit is noticed in the reduction of perceived vibration. This is the amount of vibration which you as a passenger or driver feel during operation of the engine. The counterweight can cut this to a minimum and reduce your discomfort accordingly.

The crankshaft itself can be balanced in the conventional sense. Parts for the various cylinders must each have an equal weight and all parts must be exactly spaced at equal intervals around the crankshaft. All rod journals and all counterweights must generate balancing forces to match their counterparts.

An example would be the 3 cylinder crankshaft which must have everything spaced 120 degrees apart or the V-6 crankshaft which should have 60 degree spacing between opposing forces. By doing this we have balanced the shaft as a whole but we have not ended stray or uneven forces in the crankshaft.

The counterweight on the crankshaft runs in opposition to the piston but it cannot run in line with the piston. The counterweight is offset to the side, thus the opposing forces are not in line with each other. This creates a separate loading on the crankshaft due to the misalignment. The rod journals are not directly in line with each other and this creates another misalignment of the opposing or balancing forces in the crankshaft. These misaligned forces affect the crankshaft with small distortions in all directions.

This is one of the many reasons the metal in the crankshaft requires toughness to be satisfactory. It must be able to resist the tendency to misalign to any large degree or it would fail. Indeed, some do break.

When the two-stroke crankshaft fails it may be due to that very vibration we seek to balance or counterbalance. Vibration has a frequency which is the number of oscillations in one second. It has a strength or amplitude which is another measure of its effect on surrounding objects.

All metals are sensitive to vibration. At the proper frequency and amplitude, every metal will fail. Thus, if the crankshaft is exposed to the exact required conditions of frequency, amplitude, and time, it will fail. This period of time is generally less than a minute.

In the first part of this chapter I described rotating and reciprocating weights. We also learned that the weight of the connecting rod is shared in part by each group. The small end goes up and down and the big end goes round and round. There is a point along the length of the rod where this change occurs.

The weight from that point to each side, all the way to the big or small end of the rod belongs either to the rotating mass or reciprocating mass. At one time we were forced to make painful and lengthy mathematical calculations to establish this point, and assign the proper portions of the connecting rod to each division, reciprocating mass or rotating mass.

We had to have this figure to know how much weight to counterbalance and how much weight to allow for balance. The calculation was dependent upon the length of the rod, the shape of its cross section, and a number of other considerations.

None of these were easily established and much time could be lost in the process. Today a computer does the calculations quickly and easily.

The final consideration is the flywheel and is an important part of the engine. It rotates with the crankshaft so it must be balanced with the crankshaft if the assembly is to be considered complete.

The flywheel is usually balanced alone and this is considered good enough for the stock engine. At this stage of balance it leaves a bit to be desired but literally thousands of these units have been used with longevity.

In bygone years the two-stroke engine tended to break more crankshafts in the upper main bearing than they do today. The answer was to increase the diameter of the crankshaft at the top main bearing and increase the bearing support at this point. Many different models from several manufacturers had this type of change made to them, over the years.

Whether vibration from the flywheel was responsible for the failures in those early model engines or whether the crankshaft was simply not strong enough to handle normal loads is debatable. Remember, we are talking about vibration frequencies of a very high order with a number of variables.

Whenever any model engine displayed a propensity toward early crankshaft failure, another model would appear in a year or two with a larger main bearing surface and diameter at the top of the crankshaft.

Like any engine, the cylinders and pistons of a two-stroke engine are sure to wear.

When pistons and cylinder bores wear to the point that the cylinder must be rebored and a larger piston installed you would expect this to disturb the balance of a stock engine but this is not the case.

Piston manufacturers are aware of those balance/counterbalance problems and they make oversize piston at the same weight as the original. Thus the engine which was balanced before the replacement will be balanced after.

Custom balanced, racing engines have the piston weight in grams, provided with the engine. The original maker of the piston can easily provide a replacement piston in an oversized bore with the same weight as the original.

This matter of balance and counterbalance is a fascinating study. Get an outboard crankshaft and look at the features which we have described. Try to get a picture in your mind of the forces which grow with every increase in speed and push or pull on the crankshaft when it is in operation

The stock two-cycle engine is built to close tolerances and the balance is entirely adequate for the intended purpose. The factories can not improve on the standard balancing process within the budget constraints imposed by marketing concerns.

If you are going to get a custom balance job it will cost a good deal of money and you had better know your engine builder. The balance of an engine should not be approached in a casual manner.

CHAPTER SEVEN

IGNITION SYSTEMS

Ignition systems for the two-stroke engine are exotic and produce very high voltage indeed. The early engines had a magneto ignition with points, a coil, and condenser. The modern name for the condenser is "capacitor."

A stator plate supported the coils and ignition points. The flywheel covered the magneto. There was a permanent magnet fastened to the inside perimeter of the flywheel and this magnet would rotate as the engine turned.

The two-stroke has one ignition coil for every cylinder. Construction of these coils is rather interesting in itself. The coil has a high tension winding which employs many turns of wire and is wound around the outside of the low tension winding.

There is no direct contact between these two windings. There is a baked-on varnish or insulation which isolates the wires from each other. The core is laminated metal that also serves as the mounting bracket for the coil. The mounting bolts are threaded through the ends of these laminations. The ends of the laminations are the poles for the coils. The laminations are seated on a set of pylons cast into the stator plate and held in place by mounting bolts.

The ignition coil is no more than a transformer. A transformer cannot make current, it can only change the voltage/amperage relationship.

Voltage (V) is electrical pressure. Amperage (A) is

current. The pressure of voltage drives the current or amperage and the multiple of the two is measurable as Volt Amperes (VA). The ignition coil changes electrical current from a high amperage/low voltage mode to a high voltage/low amperage mode.

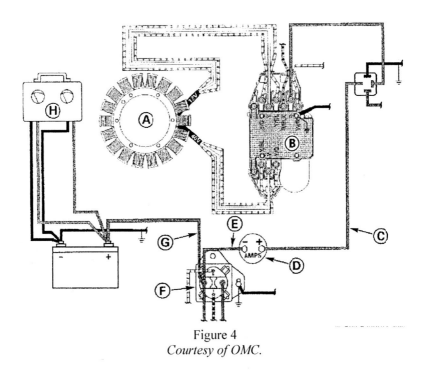

Figure 4
Courtesy of OMC.

Layout of ignition components.

It is higher voltage (greater pressure) that drives the spark to jump the plug gap, which begs two questions. First, where did the spark come from, and second, how does it change from low voltage to high voltage?

Begin with the needed current. With the ignition points closed, the rotating flywheel draws the magnet inside its perimeter across the poles on the coils. When the flux lines of the flywheel magnet are cut by the poles on the coil, the low tension side of those coils develops an electromagnetic field.

As the crankshaft continues to rotate, the points open and the electromagnetic field collapses. A current is induced in the high tension side of the coil. Induction is a process by which electrons flow from one coil winding to another, without direct contact.

The voltage is multiplied many times over in the high tension winding and discharges across the spark plug gap. The spark timing is controlled by movement of the stator plate. The plate is able to turn and change its relation to the position of the crankshaft.

This movement is accomplished by a lever operated from the throttle arm. The mechanical movement of spark and throttle provides variable timing, or spark advance, and matched it to the throttle opening.

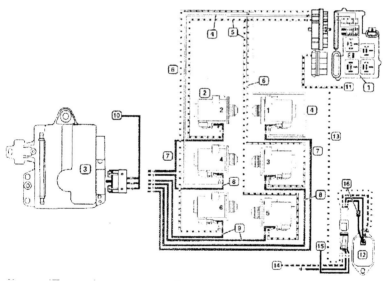

Figure 5
Courtesy of OMC.

Ignition circuit.

The spark produced by a magneto is quite hot and the magneto itself enjoys several advantages over the conventional or battery ignition systems. First, as the flywheel rotates, the input voltage to the low tension side of the coil increases and of course the output voltage improves accordingly.

Second, with one coil for every cylinder, that coil is never required to cycle or fire more than once, per revolution. This allows more time for saturating the low tension side of the coil between firing cycles. This fact, plus the higher input voltage, gives a distinct advantage to magneto ignition systems.

The spark is hotter, it gets better as the RPM increases, and it provides its own power source. No battery required. The system sounds primitive, but it is a good system.

They did a good job on those early engines but required frequent maintenance to keep the spark hot and dependable. The points had a rubbing block or cam follower built into their moving arm. This plastic piece rode on a cam or eccentric machined into the crankshaft at the top. The oblong shape was used to make and break contact between the ignition points.

Over a period of 100 hours or less, the points failed. The cam follower wore out, the grease that lubricated the cam failed or some part of the lubricant was slung into the points and their surfaces were charred. The spark was lost and the points had to be replaced.

There were other problems also. The permanent magnets in the flywheel were not always permanent. They sometimes lost a part of their magnetism and thus a good deal of the spark was lost. There was a process for restoring this magnetism without removing the magnets from the flywheel. It was called knocking the magnets and it was quite effective.

There were some engines fitted with an accessory magneto mounted as a separate unit and employing a Gates belt to drive it. The Gates belt has teeth molded onto its inner surface and the pulleys that drive it have corresponding teeth machined or cast into their outer surface. This to maintain the timing relationship between engine and spark.

These drive belts failed frequently on the early engines. Engineering improved the Gates belt and gradually it became a very reliable drive system. The timing of that belt gave some mechanics a bit of pause and the excellent directions in the service manual still did not entirely alleviate the problem.

The next generation of ignition systems was referred to as capacitive discharge ignition. This system employed two coils to produce a spark. The first coil was referred to as a charging coil. The charging coil was mounted beneath the flywheel, as before.

This coil had only one winding and it was intended to provide high amperage, low voltage current to a capacitor or condenser. The capacitor is actually a kind of storage device and it stores considerable current.

A second coil called the ignition coil was designed as before with low and high tension windings. When the ignition points broke contact, the condenser/capacitor discharged into the low tension winding of the ignition coil.

This discharge continues through the high tension windings, and is multiplied many times, then transferred to the spark plug. The ignition coil is not mounted beneath the flywheel but rather on the cylinder block, close to the individual cylinder it served.

This was an excellent system but it still had an Achilles heel in those ignition points. A better way had to be found, and it was. The next generation of ignition was referred to as a transistorized ignition.

This system employes a transistor as a switch to replace the contact points. The transistor is an electronic valve which can hold or release electrons upon demand. This transistor requires a signal to tell it when to discharge those electrons. Another coil was added inside the flywheel. This coil is referred to as a trigger coil and it has a separate magnet. We now have a charging coil to charge the capacitor, trigger coil to release the transistor, and an ignition coil to multiply the resulting voltage.

The flywheel rotates, the charging coil charges the capacitor, and the transistor holds back the charge. At the proper time, the trigger coil trips the transistor. The current in the capacitor is released into the low tension side of the ignition coil. It is then induced into the high tension side of the coil and multiplied many times. This greatly enhanced spark is delivered to the spark plug, as before.

The beauty of this system is; no points to fail, the voltage produced is quite high, about 40,000 volts, at any speed and the service life is excellent.

An electronic ignition system should run about 800 hours without service and many of them have lasted longer. There is still one more advantage to this system, and is a major force in favor of its use. The endearing quality of electronic ignition systems is their controllability.

Enter the ECM. The ECM is an Electronic Control Module and it can do all tasks, very well. The ECM is designed around a computer chip which is programmed to recognize and administer to the needs of the engine.

This device receives inputs from numerous sensors and can be told if the engine is cold or hot, loaded or unloaded, running in detonation or operating normally. It knows what to do for the engine under any of the conditions and times the spark accordingly.

The ECM can vary when the transistor trips. It can provide a spark at virtually any timing and at any RPM. Further, it can coordinate this spark with the output of an injector.

There is one other ignition system, the light beam trigger system. This unit varies from others only in the manner of tripping the transistor. The operation of this unit is accomplished with a rotor or shade which has precise holes through its sides.

As it rotates, a light beam is exposed, through the shades, and onto a sensor. The sensor sends a signal to the transistor and electrons are released from the capacitor into the low tension side of the coil. This system has had problems in the past with stray RF (Radio Frequency) emissions from spark plugs and other sources.

In fact, many of the early ECMs had a problem of their

own. They sometimes reacted to erroneous inputs. Emissions from other electronic devices could disrupt their function, radio transmissions, high voltage power lines, etc. Remember, that small computer chip is operating on very low voltage instructions and small amounts of stray current could disrupt its operation. Stray current was able to trip the transistor and provide a spark at the wrong time.

The answer to this was electronic shielding and the industry spent millions in an effort to perfect it. The newest versions of the electronic ignition and of the ECM are seldom troubled by stray currents.

The terrible thing about this problem is to reproduce the problem in the shop. This can not be accomplished unless the problem is stray current generated somewhere on the boat.

The computer chip on the ECM has a memory. It can tell the mechanic if its operation has been interrupted but not the source of the interruption.

The electronic ignition system is by far the best yet devised and it is here to stay. Engineers will continue to work out the few kinks. It will continue to improve because it does so many things so well.

CHAPTER EIGHT

THE CARBURETOR

A carburetor mixes air and fuel at predetermined ratios. Air and gasoline burn ideally at a 15 to 1 ratio, by weight. This means that 15 pounds of air are required to burn one pound of fuel. Variations from the ideal ratio are problematic.

When the air/fuel ratio exceeds 15 parts of air to a single part of fuel, the engine will run lean and the probable result will be piston failure. If the air/fuel ratio is less than 15 parts air to a single part of fuel the engine will run rich.

It will then load up at low speeds, idle poorly, and foul the spark plugs. It will also make heavy carbon deposits which will cause piston ring failure and probably destroy the engine. Mixture control is important on any engine. On the two-stroke engine it is vital.

There are three basic styles of carburetors used on gasoline powered engines. The slide valve or variable venturi carburetor is seldom seen on any marine application but is quite common on motorcycles and some outboard racing engines.

The down-draft carburetor draws fuel downward through a vertical intake and it is common to the four-stroke, inboard engine. The side-draft carburetor draws air sideways through a horizontal intake. The two-stroke engine generally uses the side draft carburetor because the intake of air/fuel mix comes from a side position.

What does a carburetor for a two-stroke engine look like and how does it work? I'll begin with the parts.

The carburetor has a body or skeleton. They were first made of aluminum because this metal was light, had ample strength, and was easily drilled or machined. As plastics technology emerged, some carburetor bodies were molded of thermoplastic. They had sufficient strength and could easily support the internal parts. Both materials are still in use today, on a variety of engines.

The carburetor body is fitted with a bowl into which fuel is delivered from the fuel pump. The bowl has a float which does exactly what the name implies. The float is made of cork, sheet metal, or other light material and hinged or cantilevered at one end. The float rises as the fuel level in the bowl increases and falls as the level recedes. It has a float valve which controls the flow of fuel. A needle valve sits on the upper surface of the float and rises or falls with it. The seat is screwed into the body of the carburetor and is static.

The needle is rather fat for this descriptive name but it is elongated and does have a point. The seat accepts the point of the valve to form a seal. Both needle and seat are generally made of brass but the needle may have a tip made of plastic or neoprene.

This is done to help reduce the wear that occurs between two metal surfaces in contact. It also reduces the need for an exactly machined tip on the needle. The soft ended needle will seal more readily against small imperfections in the seat.

There is an air passage, or throat, cast into the body of the carburetor. Air flows, down this passage, to the engine. On its way it passes through a venturi, or restriction, in the throat. This restriction speeds the flow of air briefly and on its downstream side it creates a pressure drop.

This reduced pressure draws fuel through a set of jets, or tubes, which gathers fuel from the carburetor bowl. The diameter of the jets controls the amount of fuel and consequently the air/fuel ratio.

There are two discs in the throat of the carburetor, one is ahead of the jets and one behind. They are properly described as butterflies. The butterfly ahead of the venturi is the choke. Closing this butterfly will richen the mixture for a cold start. The butterfly behind the venturi is the throttle. By opening or closing this butterfly the air flow to the engine is controlled which controls the speed.

Figure 6

V-6 intake system.

The butterflies are mounted on bronze shafts which pass through the carburetor throat. These shafts are named for the individual butterflies which they support. The throttle shaft and butterfly shaft are self explanatory terms. Small bolts hold these butterflies in place. They must be well secured with the small number of threads available.

In a modern, small horsepower engine, there may be a small, auxiliary, manually operated fuel pump. This small pump is mounted on the inside of the engine cowling and has a knob to operate the pump. By operating this hand pump, the operator pushes a small shot of raw gas through a tiny tube to the carburetor throat. This serves as a means of enriching the mixture for a cold start. This removes the need for a choke shaft or butterfly. It also removes one restriction from the carburetor throat. The flow is smoothed and increased accordingly.

There are other engines with a micro-electric fuel pump built into the system. This miniature pump is electrically powered and operated by pushing inward on the ignition switch during the starting process. No matter how they are powered, both pumps ultimately accomplish the same effect.

Two-stroke engines generally use a single carburetor or carburetor throat, for every cylinder. Small, low horsepower, two cylinder engines have successfully employed a single throated carburetor for both cylinders.

In fact, OMC (Outboard Marine Corporation) has made engines to 40 horsepower with two large bore cylinders that worked well on a single carburetor. The bottom cylinder always got more fuel and ran richer than the top cylinder. Spark plugs from the lower cylinders were darker when removed from the cylinders but these were very successful engines. They were rugged and there are still a number of them in use today. This type of carburetion may be wanting a bit in some areas but it is economically feasible.

Two-stroke engines with 3 or more cylinders have always had mixture control problems, unless served by an individual throat or carburetor. The individual attention to each cylinder is the rule manufacturers recognize.

The need is dictated by the nature of the two-stroke engine itself. You will better understand when we begin to put the engine into motion. Those engines, manufactured with a single carburetor to serve three or more cylinders are largely in the scrap pile now.

The two-stroke carburetor differs sharply from that of the four-stroke engine in at least one feature. The two-stroke carburetor does not have an accelerator pump. This pump is incorporated in the body of the four-stroke carburetor and operated by a link to the throttle arm.

The four-stroke engine requires this pump to richen the mixture when the throttle is opened and manifold pressure rises. The two-stroke has no such need.

This then is the source of air/fuel mix for the carbureted two-stroke. I will tackle the matter of electronic fuel injectors next. The injector is the glamour boy of modern mixture control but do not revile those carburetors. They have done a great job for many years and for some applications, they are still the only way to go.

CHAPTER NINE

FUEL INJECTION

The gasoline-powered, marine engine is moving rapidly from carburetion to Electronic Fuel Injection (EFI). The electronically controlled fuel injection system may take any one of several forms. First, it may inject the fuel into a port location. This system is the one commonly designated as EFI or Electronic Fuel Injection.

Alternatively, the fuel injector may inject its fuel directly into the cylinder of the engine, after the last port closes. This system is described as a DFI or Direct Fuel Injection. It too is electronically controlled. The DFI is the newest form of injection.

The DFI is principally represented by three different systems. The Orbital Injector, favored by Mercury/Mariner and Tohatsu/Nissan, is the first of those systems. The Ficht Injector favored by Evinrude/Johnson is the second. The High Pressure Direct Injection or HPDI developed by Yamaha Marine for its own use is the third form of DFI. All of these systems vary from each other in the amount of injector pressure they generate and in the manner in they function. I will detail both parts and operation for each of these three systems.

The EFI injector has a body which may be metal or plastic. The body is oblong in shape and about the size of a small sausage. It has a number of holes or orifices let into its surfaces to admit and discharge fuel and to accommodate electrical conductors.

The body ends in a pintle or spout. The shape and drilling of this pintle controls the flow and the pattern of fuel emerging from the injector. We call the process atomization and while it does not literally break the fuel up into atoms, it does produce very minute droplets.

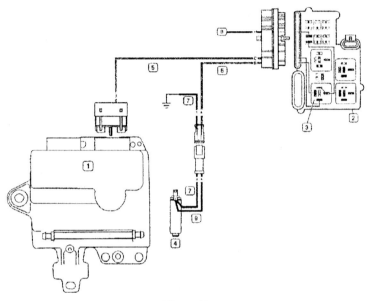

Figure 7
Courtesy of OMC

Electric fuel pump circuit.

Behind the pintle is a spring loaded, electronically controlled, valve mechanism. This valve opens in response to electronic commands or closes under spring pressure. A fuel pump provides fuel to this system through a rail which serves all the injectors on the engine.

Fuel in the common EFI system is distributed along the rail at pressures of about 35 lbs/in². This pressure is considered sufficient to atomize the fuel and improve its mixture with the incoming air supply.

The Electronic Fuel Injector can be controlled by a

simple computer chip. It also may be incorporated into an overall engine management system which we call an ECM or Electronic Control Module. This device is an onboard engine computer which receives inputs from many sources. The computer then knows the temperature, load, and speed of the engine. In fact, through its many sensors it knows everything about the engine's condition. It can then direct the spark timing, the amount of fuel to be delivered, the frequency of delivery, and manage the functions of the engine.

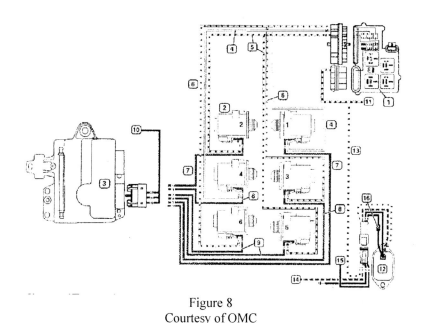

Figure 8
Courtesy of OMC

Fuel injector circuit.

Both types of fuel injector, EFI and DFI can be managed by an ECM. This precise control is the forte of the injector system. No other fuel delivery system can match this flexibility or offer the programmer so much control over injector function.

The DFI difference. The EFI system offered:

1. Fuel atomization.
2. Precise control of the mixture.
3. Timing and duration of the fuel spray.
4. Controllability.

The DFI system goes a few steps beyond.

Manufacturers of the three DFI units have differing opinions when it comes to the superiority or the most desirable characteristics of the three units. However, there are three things all of these companies tend to agree upon.

They all believe DFI gives:

1. Better fuel atomization than a simple EFI.
2. Higher injector pressures to accomplish this.
3. Injection directly into the cylinder of the engine.

This latter feature eliminates the natural tendency of the two-stroke to lose unburned fuel out of open ports.

Figure 9

Now the descriptions of the parts and function of the three DFI systems named above.

The Mercury Opti-Max fuel injection is based on technology created by the Orbital Injection Company. This unit employs a pair of fuel pumps. One is a low pressure pump which furnishes fuel at about 35 lbs/in². to a second or high pressure pump. In the high pressure pump the fuel pressure is raised to about 90 lbs/in².

The high pressure fuel pump on the Opti-Max injector provides fuel to a rail or fuel distribution system. The rail distributes this highly pressurized fuel to each injector, individually. The terminal end of the rail is attached to an orifice in the injector.

The injector screws into the cylinder head rather than the intake port. One to each cylinder. It has a body with a pintle or nozzle for discharge, and a spring loaded valve to control the fuel discharge. The injector actually employs two orifices in the body. The first is the one to admit fuel to the injector which we described in the preceding paragraph.

The second orifice is designed to admit high pressure air to the injector. An air compressor is mounted on the side of the engine block. It maintains air pressure in a small reservoir at about 80 lbs/in². The reservoir is needed to smooth pulsation from the compressor.

An air distribution manifold delivers air from the reservoir to the injectors. This manifold is a series of tubes, one for each cylinder/injector. The terminal end is attached to the second orifice in the injector body. The air pressure is controlled by a high-speed solenoid switch.

When the electronic control cycles the injector, a valve opens and admits air pressure from the manifold into the injector. The air mixes with the fuel and both are discharged from the injector pintle. The discharge enters the cylinder after the last valve is closed.

Mercury's claims are:

1. Superior atomization of the fuel.
2. A better air/fuel mix.
3. Less pollution.

4. Better fuel economy.
5. Excellent dependability.

The Ficht Injector system from OMC was also developed by an outside company and adapted to their use. The Ficht injector varies in design from the Opti-Max in several ways. They both inject directly into the cylinder but here the similarity ends.

In the Ficht system, there is a low pressure fuel pump but no separate high pressure, fuel pump from the injector body. The low pressure fuel pump provides fuel directly to each injector. The high pressure for actual injection, about 480 lbs/in^2, comes from an electromechanical solenoid incorporated directly into the fuel injector assembly.

The solenoid pulls a small piston downward against the fuel supply and drives the fuel before itself. This solenoid system has a mechanical advantage. It multiplies the fuel pressure from the low pressure pump several times, finally reaching 480 lbs/in^2. The pressure travels down the injector body to a spring loaded check valve. When the pressure is high enough it forces the valve to open and discharge through the pintle.

The entire injector/solenoid assembly sits atop the cylinder head, one for each cylinder. The injector is threaded through a hole in the top of the cylinder head and exposed to the inside of the cylinder. The solenoid responds to a signal from the ECM or Electronic Control Module and discharges into the cylinder after the last port closes.

The advantages OMC claims for its Ficht injection system are:

1. Superior atomization of the fuel.
2. Better air/fuel mix.
3. Less smoke and pollution.
4. Better fuel economy.
5. Excellent dependability.

The Yamaha DFI unit is an in house development called HPDI which stands for High Pressure Direct Injection. This unit employs a low pressure fuel pump which delivers fuel at low pressure to the high pressure injector pump. Both of these pumps are separate from the injectors.

The high pressure fuel pump delivers fuel to a rail or set of tubes which delivers this highly pressurized fuel to the injector. It enters through an orifice in the side of the injector. A valve in the fuel system controls the highly pressurized fuel and an electromechanical solenoid controls the valve.

When the ECM cycles this valve, it will discharge into the injector nozzle at 700 lbs/in^2. This is by far the highest working injector pressure in use on any gasoline-powered engine today. The injector body is threaded through the cylinder head and into the cylinder. It discharges through the pintle into the cylinder, after the last valve closes.

Yamaha Marine claims are:

1. The highest injector pressure of any system presently in operation.

2. Better atomization of the fuel, due to extreme pressure.

3. Better fuel economy.

4. Less pollution.

5. Good dependability.

All of these DFI systems have at least one common and endearing characteristic. They cure the classic stumble which two-strokes tend to develop at idle or at speeds slightly above idle. This phenomenon occurs in all loop charged engines and in many cross port engines.

The reason for this problem has to do with the tendency of the incoming air/fuel charge to be partially lost through the open exhaust port at low speeds.

I do believe all the DFI systems described, achieve the claimed advantages when compared to older carbureted engines. How they compare to each other, requires far more discussion than any book can hold.

They all work well but each has problems of its own. The designs of all three have inherent areas of superiority and areas of less than admirable performance as well. The entire DFI concept is in the early stages of development, and will undoubtedly, improve with age.

CHAPTER TEN

TWO-STROKE VALVES

The internal combustion engine, whether two-stroke or four-stroke, is no more than an air pump. In order to produce power it is designed to pump both air and a combustible fuel but it is still a pump. The two-stroke engine has no intake or exhaust valves in the classic sense.

Having no valves, it has no need of a camshaft, cam followers, rocker arms, nor valve springs. Yet, it must have some means to achieve control of the air flow and the direction of that flow in order to work as a pump. Historically, the two-stroke engine has used several types of valving to achieve a number of different flow requirements.

The first and the most elementary of these valving systems really has no valves at all. Rather it incorporates an arrangement of ports or passages to achieve the needed fuel/air transfer. There are ports let into the sides of the cylinders and piston skirts.

The alignment or misalignment of these ports decides the open or closed position for each port. There are two separate functions they perform. One set of these ports is referred to as intake ports while the other is referred to as exhaust ports. The names describe the function of each.

Intake ports take air/fuel mix into the cylinder. Exhaust ports let the burned gasses out of the cylinder. Transfer ports or bypass ports (either name is acceptable) transfer fuel from the crankcase to the combustion chamber when the appropriate ports align in piston and cylinder.

The height of the ports in the cylinder bore provides timing for the valve system. The valve-open valve-closed events the camshaft establishes for the four-stroke engine are controlled by porting in the two-stroke engine. The two-stroke engine has duration, the total time the port is open, as does the four-stroke engine, which is the total time the valve is open. It has overlap, which is the total time both ports are open at the same moment, just as the four-stroke has overlap, which is the time when both valves are open.

However, the two-stroke engine does not have a lift figure to consider as does the four-stroke because there are no camshaft operated valves.

How does the two-stroke get its port timing? Degrees of crankshaft travel are translated into piston height, then measured on the cylinder walls and the port position is established. The crankshaft degrees for each event, port-open or port-closed on intake or exhaust, can be measured with a degree wheel and the timing taken from the engine just as we do with a camshaft on a four-stroke.

In the cross-flow engine, these ports, intake and exhaust, are arranged on opposite sides of the cylinder. In the loop-charged engine they are arranged all about. Most of the loop-charged engines in use today are actually what I think of as a 3/4 loop. They have intake ports on two sides of the cylinder, opposite each other. They also have a single set of exhaust ports on one side of the cylinder at 90 degrees from a line through the middle of the intake ports. This gives rise to my designation of a 3/4 engine since the potential exists for another set of exhaust ports opposite the present set.

The loop-charging system uses a small number of smaller ports scattered about the cylinder. The cross port engine concentrates a larger number of smaller ports in a cluster and the supporting space between the ports is called webbing. Port webbing and their spacing are important since they help to keep the piston rings under control.

It is possible to operate a two-stroke engine with no

valving other than can be accomplished by porting in cylinder wall and piston skirt. As the piston moves up and down in the cylinder bore it covers or uncovers the ports in a predetermined sequence.

Ultimately, sets of ports and passages are sufficient to accomplish all of the valving necessary to two-stroke operation. This is perhaps the simplest of engines and it works very effectively. It has the fewest moving parts and it is economical to build.

Figure 10

Reed valves.

An engine which employs this system is referred to as a piston port engine. They were common in the '30s and '40s and the Volvo Corporation introduced one a bit later. The engines were around for several years but the piston port engine is seldom seen today.

This engine has an Achilles heel that plagues it continuously. The problem lies in the transfer ports. The intake and exhaust ports are above the piston rings and the seal is very positive since the rings themselves provide the necessary pressure control. The transfer port is in the piston skirt and below the piston rings. The piston skirt alone makes the seal and it requires a very close fit between the piston and the cylinder wall in order to retain a gas under pressure.

This gives rise to three problems for the piston port engine. First, the engine requires greater amounts of oil in the premix to maintain that close piston to wall tolerance. Second, it must run cool so that heat expansion will not cause the piston to drag the cylinder walls.

The first two problems give rise to the third. Piston port engines are hard on pollution controls. This is a truly dirty engine. It is also a short-lived machine. The first time you lean down the premix or run the engine hot for even a short time, the seal may be lost.

The transfer ports are essential to good engine operation. They transfer air/fuel mix from the crankcase upward into the cylinder. In the early stages of failure a leak at these ports will only cause hard starting and a rough idle. In the latter stages it may cause the engine to lean out and stick a piston.

In preference to the piston port system, a number of alternatives have been developed. The first of these was called a rotary valve and this is an excellent system. There were both internal rotors and external rotors. The external rotor being far superior in terms of performance and efficiency.

The internal rotor system started with a hole in the crankcase. The carburetor was bolted over the face of this hole. Inside the engine there was a rotating portion of the crankshaft which had a hole drilled into it. When the hole in the crankshaft lined up with the hole in the crankcase, air flowed into the engine.

Timing the flow was controlled by the location of the two holes. This was a simple system but it too was subject to early failure. It depended upon the clearance between the aluminum case and the crankshaft to maintain the seal. The soft aluminum case and the movement of the crankshaft created a good deal of wear on the sealing surfaces.

The external rotary valve system is efficient, durable, and operates at very high RPM.

The external rotor employs a thick disc within a flat housing. The disc is driven by a gear or belt. Holes machined in the rotating disc align with those in the flat housing to provide a seal or opening. The timing is controlled by the relative shapes and by teeth in either the belt or gear which drives the system.

I have saved the best for last. The reed valve is by far the most prevalent valving system in the history of the two-stroke engine. The reed valve is sometimes referred to as a demand valve.

This valve is simplicity itself. Begin with a housing or cage which is the body of the valve system. It may have any one of several shapes but the sealing surface that forms the valve will always be flat, with a machined, thumb-shaped slot.

The reed itself is also flat. It is thumb shaped on one end and square on the other. It is manufactured of spring steel, a very strong plastic, or in the high performance engine, a carbon fiber material. These reeds are usually about .012 inch in thickness. This is the reed itself.

The square shaped end of the thumb/reed is bolted to the reed plate. This leaves the rounded end of the thumb/reed free. The entire length of the reed is lying flat against the surface of the cage.

The reed cage is bolted across the opening in the crankcase with the reed facing inward towards the engine. When the piston rises, pressure drops in the crankcase. That pressure drop is on the reed side of the plate. The reed is lifted and air/fuel mix admitted. When the piston ceases to rise, the pressure equalizes. The spring pressure in the reed itself causes the reed to fall back onto the plate and as the pressure continues to rise the reed-to-plate covering forms a seal against the pressure.

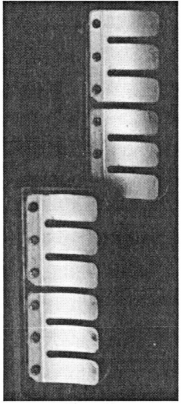

Figure 11

Reed stops.

A curved reed stop is used as a limiting device for the reed valve. The reed stop is a very stout and inflexible metal. It is bolted on top of, and curves away from the thumb end of the reed. When opening, the reed rises against the growing pressure of the reed stop and is prevented from damaging itself or other engine parts.

The fact that this valve opens and closes in response to demands or pressure changes in the engine gives rise to the name demand valve. This is a low cost, easily made, and very efficient system that seldom fails and often outlasts the engine.

Figure 12

Yamaha reed valve system.

The only valving system you are likely to see today is the reed valve. Yet it is instructive to consider the other types of valves and if you are a racing fan or a student of antique engines you may well encounter one of the others.

I want to end this chapter with a reference that may improve your understanding of porting in a cylinder. This comparison will be especially helpful to those of you who are four-cycle mechanics.

I'll begin with the features of the valve timing in a four-stroke engine and then explore the two-stroke comparison.

The valve open and valve closed events in a four-stroke engine correspond to the port open and port closed events in a two-stroke engine. The total time, measured in crankshaft degrees, that the valve is open on a four-stroke engine is referred to as duration. The total time, measured in crankshaft degrees, a port is open on the two-stroke engine, is also referred to as duration.

The time, measured in crankshaft degrees, when both valves are open simultaneously is referred to as overlap on the four-stroke engine. The total time, measured in crankshaft degrees, when both ports are open simultaneously is referred to as overlap on the two-stroke engine.

Get a cam card from any speed shop and look at the series of events depicted on the card. Consider the ideas offered in the last few paragraphs. Visualize them in the light of the illustration and you will more easily understand porting and its effects.

CHAPTER ELEVEN

LUBRICATING SYSTEMS

Lubricating systems for the two-stroke engine were never controversial until the 1980s. Prior to 1981, all two-stroke engines sold in the United States were designed for premix lubrication. The oil was mixed with the fuel in varying proportions. The oil entered the engine with the air/fuel mix and was distributed among the parts by those swirling gasses in the crankcase.

The system was adequate for lubrication but it left a bit to be desired in terms of passenger comfort. The engine smoked and that smoke caused coughing, teary eyed passengers. Why so dirty? Consider the amount of oil in the fuels.

A common figure for premixing oil in the 1940s was 25:1 or 25 parts of gasoline to a single part of lubricant. The common language description was, A quart to six gallons. Oil from the exhaust actually made a film on the water.

By the early 1960s this ratio had dropped to 50:1. That is 50 parts of gasoline to a single part of lubricant or a 1 pint to six gallon ratio. The change was made possible by changes in engine design and improvements in the lubricants themselves. Still the engine smoked excessively.

The premixing of fuels caused a number of other problems as well. Large capacity fuel tanks are always a necessity for larger outboards.

A part of the problem was evaporation. The fuel

remaining in large tanks tended to evaporate a bit at a time, but the two-cycle oil did not. Gradually, the remaining fuel supply became increasingly oil rich. Of course, this exacerbated the smoking problem.

To make matters worse, few boaters rarely measured the oil they added to the gasoline. The result was a fuel blend that was either oil rich or oil lean. The boater faced that problem without solution until 1982.

In 1982 the Suzuki Marine Company brought the first automatic oiling system to this country. This early system used a pump which had an amazing resemblance to parts taken from a two-stroke motorcycle engine. It also utilized an oil reservoir affixed to the engine block and located beneath the cowling.

Oil was gravity fed from the under cowl tank to the oil delivery pump. The pump then delivered measured amounts of lubricant to a set of individual tubes that ended in the separate intake systems for each cylinder. In a carbureted engine the oil was picked up in the flow of air/fuel mix and delivered to the crankcase.

The only difference between carbureted engines and fuel injected engines was there was no gasoline in the air that entered the crankcase. The oil that was injected, rode on a stream of air alone, rather than air and fuel together.

The oil rode into the crankcase on this high speed stream of air or air/fuel mix. It was atomized as before and distributed to all the moving parts. This method solved three problems at once.

First, oil from this system was provided to the engine in exact amounts, thus the oil to fuel ratio was always correct.

Second, the pump was designed to vary the oil to fuel ratio as the speed of the engine changed. It provided a variable oil ratio that was richer (more oil to a given amount of fuel) at high speeds and leaner (less oil to a given amount of fuel) at low speeds. Thus the total amount of oil consumed was less.

The third advantage to this method of operation was the stabilizing effect on the fuel in the tank. There was no tendency to build a cumulative oil ratio error into the fuel supply because only raw gasoline was in storage. This was a very significant breakthrough and one that Suzuki probably did not advertise as aggressively as they might have.

Yamaha Marine brought their own automatic oiling system to this country in 1984. At that time I was riding an old Yamaha RD 350 motorcycle and I remember looking at the oil pumps on the new outboard engines and those on my RD 350. If they were not a pair of clones you could have fooled me.

Figure 13

The gear on this Mercury crankshaft drive the oil pump.

Both foreign manufacturers, Suzuki and Yamaha had done their homework on oil pumps some years before. The systems were well perfected before they were introduced into this country. We in the United States were not so lucky. Early efforts to build an automatic oiling system by American manufacturers ended in disaster.

United States manufacturers employed a separate, remote oil reservoir that was mounted in the vessel. There was no reservoir on the engine and the oil pump had to bring fuel from the remote tank and distribute it in metered amounts to the various cylinders as well. The pump was powered by a diaphragm that responded to changes in pressure within the crankcase.

A tube from the crankcase entered the pump above the

diaphragm and as the crankcase compression varied, up and down, the diaphragm responded accordingly. This movement of the diaphragm pulled against two, one-way valves and pumped oil from the reservoir.

Those early oil pumps suffered a number of shortcomings and the result was so bad that remote oiling systems became suspect. Boaters began to reject the system that would finally prove to be immensely popular and even necessary to improved performance. Automatic oiling really was a great idea, but it nearly died. Even the ones which worked well were greeted with skepticism.

Mechanics found it was possible to block off the oil ports on a two-stroke engine and revert to premixing the fuel. The engine still ran fine but it was very dirty. We were just beginning to get the bugs out of these oiling systems when the first fuel injectors made their appearance.

The big push was beginning to clean up the two-stroke exhaust. It would be necessary to have that variable ratio oil delivery system if we were to take full advantage of the fuel injector. Another major breakthrough that helped to make the leaner and cleaner two-stroke possible was the recirculating oil system.

Oil mixed with flowing air or air/fuel mix tended to cling to the inside of the crankcase and to puddle at the bottom of each cylinder. In the early engine, this oil was dumped out through a one-way valve in the bottom cylinder and entered the exhaust where it discharged.

The recirculation system used crankcase pressures to lift this puddled oil from the lower cylinders and deliver it upward through tiny passages to the upper cylinders to be used again. This utilized the oil that entered the engine to its fullest potential and made it possible to use leaner mixtures.

There have never been two-stroke injectors that delivered premix. The oil is delivered to the crankcase and atomized with the incoming air. In the newest Direct Fuel Injection (DFI) units, the oil is never mixed with the gasoline before it enters the cylinder. Thus the lubricity of the oil is never diluted.

The variable ratio pump compliments the operation of the DFI unit and greatly increases the efficiency. As I write this book, technology is chasing inspiration and new ideas are coming rapidly. Mercury Marine has built a multi-point, electronic oil injector which appears to be the first of its kind. This electronic oil injector provides measured amounts of oil to the needed areas, according to the programmed directions of the ECM.

The two-stroke engine is said to change its oil on every revolution and this is an apt description. New oil enters the crankcase every time the engine turns over and the old oil is passed through the exhaust, at the same time. There are advantages to this system but it also has a few pitfalls.

An empty crankcase makes for a unique set of requirements and the detergent package for a two-stroke lubricant is vastly different from that of a four-stroke engine.

First, there are no acids accumulating in the oil reservoir or crankcase. Second, the engine has no oil pump and it must work oil into the bearings at every start up. This makes it necessary to use an oil with strong coating properties, one that clings to every surface. That residue is needed to keep the parts from wearing excessively when the engine first turns over.

The two-stroke may be stored for long periods of time during which its owner largely ignores the beast. Owners manuals suggest the proper ways to store the two-stroke engine but these suggestions are often ignored. The manufacturers of our lubricants are well aware of this and every effort is made to deter the formation of rust in a crankcase that has no oil bath.

Early engines often used bushings in the connecting rods and these bushings did not oil well without pressure lubrication. The engine was limited in speed (RPM) by those early bushings. Roller bearings are ideally suited for airborne lubricants because of the open nature of the bearing itself. That connecting rod is flying around in an atomized, oil laden, atmosphere.

Believe it or not, an oil pump on a four-stroke engine consumes a considerable amount of horsepower. It takes about 4 to 4.5 horsepower to operate the oil pump on an average auto engine. Some require even more horsepower to keep the engine lubricated. The two-stroke engine can use this horsepower to drive your boat since it has no such pump.

CHAPTER TWELVE

EXHAUST SYSTEM

The exhaust system is a very important part of a two-cycle engine. It can add as much as 25 percent to the horsepower of a stock engine and even more to that of a racing engine. If you want the engine to sing that song of power the pipes must be in perfect tune. Believe it or not, sound and inertia make the whole thing work.

Let us begin on the power stroke. There is a fresh and burning charge in the cylinder. Pressure is forcing the piston downward. Now the exhaust ports open in the side of the block. Exhaust gasses begin to exit the ports. At first blush it would seem the best possible situation would be wide open air which would discharge the exhaust gasses with no back pressure.

Actually it does not work that way. Let us add a pipe to the exhaust side of the engine. We can dump the emerging gasses into this pipe and build a flow direction. The gasses have mass or weight and they are affected by inertia. When they begin to move in a particular direction they tend to continue to move.

Now we open the intake ports to allow fuel into the cylinder. The incoming air/fuel charge also has weight and it too is being hustled along by pressure and inertial forces. The two systems, the intake system and the exhaust system, are each helping the other along. Thus, a pipe of proper diameter to maintain velocity in the flow is beneficial.

Go back to the beginning of the power stroke when the exhaust gasses, first began to emerge. Along with these gasses comes a sonic or sound wave. The sound wave can produce pressure, either positive or negative. In this instance, the pressure wave is moving down the pipe and it has a positive value. It is pushing exhaust gasses before it.

We now have three systems working for us. The intake has an established flow direction, the exhaust has an established flow direction, and the sonic from the combustion is pushing the exhaust out of the engine. The rule says, if the sonic reaches the end of the pipe and meets no resistance, it will return up the pipe with an opposite value -- negative value.

This negative value pulls exhaust gasses out of the cylinder. The sonic should arrive at the port at the exact moment the port is about to close. If it is properly timed the result can be awesome. The cylinder is scavenged of all burned gasses and the new charge retained within the engine.

If it is early or late it will interfere with the flow of unburned gasses, coming into the cylinder. It can either drive some of the fresh charge back into the crankcase or it may draw some of that fresh charge out through the exhaust ports. Either situation is bad for engine performance.

The timing of sonic response is controlled by the length of the exhaust pipe and for this reason it is very important that all the exhaust pipes have an equal length. Only in this manner can each cylinder be charged evenly and the engine will perform smoothly

The tuned exhaust is sometimes described as an extractor exhaust since it helps to extract the emerging exhaust gas. The most graphic portrayal of an extractor exhaust is the automotive header. Look at a set of headers and you can easily see the inertia pipe and the megaphone on the end.

Those tortured shapes in the pipes are made in an effort to get exactly even lengths for each pipe and an equal distance from the megaphone to each cylinder. Each of those convoluted bends cause restricted flow in the pipe. It is obvious, how much importance is placed on perfectly equal pipe length.

The highly tuned exhaust system has many potential benefits but there are several problems which arise because of it. The speed at which the sonic wave travels varies with the RPM of the engine. Open the throttle and the sonic changes speeds. Close the throttle and it changes speeds again. We need a variable length in the exhaust pipes if we are to get the system tuned to perfection.

Figure 14

Tuned exhaust housing.

There is no practical way to change the length of the exhaust pipe during changes in speed, thus no way to tune the exhaust for all operating RPM. The choice we are faced with is simple: do without the pipe, or accept the fact it will work well at some speeds and not so well at others. In most of the two-stroke engines of today, we have chosen the latter.

We know very well the exhaust system is a hindrance at low speeds but it really does a great job as the RPM increases. This is the reason for the pipe engines we often get on our transom. They tend not to idle too smoothly as the pipe resonates out of phase and the carburetor does not meter properly. The engine still bucks a bit at speeds around 1,500 RPM for the same reason but as the speed begins to climb, hang on. At about 2,500 RPM the pipe begins to tune in to the engine speed and by the time you have reached 3,000 RPM the two assemblies, engine and exhaust, are singing like the Sunday choir.

This is a very basic description of the function of a tuned exhaust pipe but there are other interesting features to consider. Begin with shape. The pipe is seldom shaped with straight sides but more like a megaphone with a tapered opening. This taper serves a purpose.

The megaphone shape in the exhaust pipe amplifies the sonic wave from our exhaust so the scavenging effect is greater on the unburned gasses. This is both a help and a hindrance.

Again, when the pipe resonates in phase the result is very helpful but if the pipe is out of tune it hurts the performance of the engine. To aggravate the problems of tuning the system, there are many uncontrollable factors which affect the operation of the sonic wave. Temperature, relative humidity, and a number of other factors control the speed of the movement.

Generally, the engine operates at a controlled temperature and the pipe is immersed in the drive shaft housing where temperature can be somewhat controlled. Nothing can be done about relative humidity in the air or barometric pressure in the atmosphere. Variables are responsible for engines that seem to run better on some days than others.

The shape and design of the cylinder block places restrictions on the design of the pipe. It is not possible to get pipes exactly the same length in the system and some cylinders operate in closer tune than others. Cylinders are charged differently and this can cause a lean/rich fuel distribution.

It has been necessary to change carburetor jetting on the individual cylinders of some engines and alter the compression ratio of an individual cylinder to allow for lean conditions. For all its inherent faults, the tuned exhaust still provides a lot of horsepower.

In the chapter on cylinder types I described the cross port and the loop charged cylinders. Tuned exhaust systems play the same role in the operation of both cross port and loop charged cylinders but they effect each in a slightly different way. So much for the stock engine.

Onto the real screamers. The four-or-five-horsepower-per-cubic-inch jobs that set the water on fire at century plus speeds? On a racing engine with an open exhaust this baby will really strut!

Given free reign to innovate, the designer can produce pipes of equal length, a wide angle megaphone to get more amplification, and inertia piping that will pull like a tractor. Tuned to perfection, the pipe can do amazing things. But hold on.

Even here, there is still a problem. A megaphone can not only strengthens the return wave, it can spread the effect across a greater number of RPM. But even in the best of circumstances, the pipe only resonates in phase across a narrow RPM band. This is true regardless of the engine's potential.

The beneficial effect of a tuned exhaust system can be spread across approximately 3,000 RPM, no more. If the engine turns 6,000 RPM, the pipe is working well for half that spread. If the engine turns 12,000 RPM the pipe will still operate properly for only the top 3,000 RPM.

This is the reason highly tuned, two-stroke motorcycles have numerous gears. Those gear changes keep the engine turning in the RPM band, regardless of the bike's speed. We boaters, on the other hand, have no such gear changes and when our tuned exhaust systems resonate out of phase, we say the engine is bogging down.

As the speed increases we suddenly find our engine has come alive. You are going to lose power if you overload the two-stroke and this is why the correct prop is so important.

The tuned exhaust system is a true Jekyll and Hyde story but nobody ignores the value of this power maker when they design an engine. I owe a good deal to Roger Huntington, an old timer at *HOT ROD* Magazine for expanding my horizons on this subject. More came from the late John Peek of Port Arthur, Texas. John designed and built the *PEEK WILDCAT* engines and I worked with him for several years.

An unexpected bit of help came from a Japanese engineer who worked for the Yamaha Corporation. When I asked him about the source of his insightful comments on this subject he smiled and said, "We are interested in sonics and remember, we have a music company." There is a Yamaha organ, sure enough.

The pipes are actually individual megaphones that do amplify sound and there is a comparative physical similarity between the exhaust and the organ. Engines are the most wonderful things that I know about and the more you learn about them the more you want to know. That knowledge sometimes comes from unexpected places.

CHAPTER THIRTEEN

HOW THE ENGINE RUNS

We have well detailed the parts of the engine and their separate functions. Now it is time to put those parts together and see if they will run. I am going to start this process with a brief preview of engine operation and then expand upon the finer points of two-stroke functions.

Start with a two-stroke engine and assume it has only a single cylinder for simplicity of description. In order to run, this engine will require an air/fuel mix in the proper proportion. It will need compression and a spark provided at the proper time. To accomplish these things the engine will require every one of those parts I have detailed.

I will begin with an example of operation that applies to all two-stroke engines. Next, we will consider carbureted engines only, then approach the differences that occur in the Electronic Fuel Injection (EFI) systems and in the Direct Fuel Injected (DFI) systems. The following applies to all two-stroke engines.

The engine will go through five cycles in a single revolution. Each of those five cycles is necessary and they must occur in sequence at the proper time. Those cycles are: Intake, Compression, Power, Exhaust and Transfer. Intake and compression occur on the upward stroke of the piston while power and exhaust occur on the down stroke. The transfer cycle occurs between the exhaust stroke and the intake stroke.

This may seem a bit confusing but in a few moments it

will make sense. The next few paragraphs will consider only the carbureted engine.

The piston is about 15 degrees ahead of top dead center, the cylinder has a fresh air/fuel charge inside. The compression on the charge is proper and we have a good spark. Another charge of air/fuel mix is contained in the crankcase of the engine. We are ready to begin operation.

At this point the spark plug fires. The fuel ignites, pressure builds in the cylinder. The piston carries over top dead center and begins to travel downward on the power/exhaust stroke. Several things will happen in the following order:

1. The piston will be forced downward against the crankshaft.

2. The crankshaft will begin to turn.

3. The falling piston will create pressure on the crankcase below.

4. As the piston drops further down in the cylinder bore, the exhaust ports will uncover and the burned gasses will enter the exhaust pipe.

5. The piston will continue to fall and the intake ports will be uncovered.

6. Pressure on the crankcase, built by the falling piston, will force a fresh air/fuel charge upward into the open cylinder.

7. The piston will come up on the intake/compression stroke.

As the piston rises to cover both ports it will begin compression again. It will continue to compress until it approaches top dead center and there the power stroke will begin once more. The most difficult and the most important thing to understand in this process is the transfer cycle.

Remember the piston in this engine makes a pressure change both above and below the piston. On the upstroke a pressure drop will occur in the crankcase, below the piston, and a pressure increase will occur in the combustion chamber above the piston top.

On the down stroke, the piston will cause a pressure drop in the combustion chamber, above its top, and a pressure increase below the piston, in the crankcase. On the upstroke, pressure drop occurs in the crankcase and the reed valves will open. This will allow air/fuel mix to enter the engine. On the down stroke the pressure will rise in the crankcase and the reed valves will seal.

As the piston continues to move downward, pressure on the crankcase will continue to build until the intake ports open. Then the pressure on the crankcase drives the fuel upward into the cylinder. This is the transfer cycle we mentioned earlier and you must understand this cycle if you are ever to understand two-cycle operation.

The transfer cycle is needed because the engine has no valves in the cylinder. Without this pressure from the crankcase the two-stroke engine would not breathe. It simply would not be capable of taking an air/fuel charge and for this reason we must both employ and understand the transfer cycle.

The second consideration is the matter of spark timing. You will notice the engine fired at about 15 degrees before top dead center. This timing is called lead, or more commonly, advance. Firing the engine early, causes some back pressure against the rising piston and actually wastes a bit of fuel, but it is necessary.

This early ignition allows the pressure in the cylinder to build to maximum intensity when the piston is at top dead center. If the engine did not fire until it was at top dead center, much of the fuel would still be burning when the exhaust port opened and wasted.

The optimum time for the spark to arrive depends upon the speed of the engine and the load. The 15 degree advance we used for our illustration would occur at half speed. Idle speeds would require less advance, while top speeds would require more.

The principal differences in the operation of EFI engines involves the manner in which fuel is delivered to the engine. Fuel does not pass through the crankcase, rather it is delivered to the air stream in the transfer ports. Only air is taken into the crankcase. When the air is transferred through the transfer ports, the fuel is injected into the air stream. The charge, which is supplied to the cylinder, already has fuel mixed with the air.

The DFI system varies, again, in that it has no fuel mixed in with the air until the last port on the engine is closed. The injector is mounted directly on top of the cylinder and injects its fuel after the ports close and before compression pressure is developed inside the cylinder.

I have not dwelled upon the operation of the tuned exhaust system in this description as I trust this function will be fresh in your mind from the last chapter. I want to discuss the torque/horsepower relationship as it applies to this engine.

I would urge you to go review the early chapters and the individual parts of the engine I have described and the manner in which each operates. Plug those description into the running sequence and you will understand how each part contributes to the whole.

Visualize the air as it passes through the carburetor intake, through the venturi, and picks up the fuel. Trace it through the reed valves, into the crankcase, and upward into the cylinder. Think about the ignition system as it builds EMF (electromotive force) and throws a spark across the plug gap. The fire begins in the cylinder, the fuel burns, and the pressure builds on the piston. Pressure on the piston turns the crankshaft as the piston falls. Think about the ports in the side of the cylinder. As you review these movements you will begin to see one truth. The engine is a combination of highly complex systems, all performing in unison.

Think about the air flow across the engine. The intake system compliments the exhaust system. The exhaust system assists the performance of the intake system. The two work in unison to maintain a smooth and balanced flow.

When any portion of the system fails to maintain that balance, the engine as a whole suffers. If the pipe resonates out of phase, even for a moment, engine performance suffers markedly. The same is true of any other system in the engine. We must maintain harmony between all the parts, if the engine is to hum.

There are two things we have not touched upon in this chapter. The first is the matter of cross port intake systems versus loop charged intake systems. With regard to general operating theory, they work the same. When you consider the manner in which they accomplish the intake of the fresh charge and the removal of the spent gasses, there is a vast difference.

The difference has to do with the shape of the incoming charge, how the air fuel mix is distributed about the combustion chamber, and how the fuel is burned after ignition. This discussion belongs in the area of flame propagation which is the subject of our next chapter.

There is however a second subject which belongs, at least in part with this chapter; torque. We are discussing engine operation and torque is certainly an inseparable part of the operation of any piston engine.

Begin with the nature of torque. Torque is twisting movement. It is measured in foot pounds and written as lbs/ft A foot pound of torque is defined as a one pound force, applied to a lever, at one foot distance from the centerline of a shaft. Torque is a potential. You will notice in the definition there is no movement and no element of time. Torque does no work. Torque alone will not turn a shaft or drive a propeller. This is the function of horsepower. Horsepower is measured in foot pounds of work. One horsepower will lift 33,000 pounds, one foot, in one minute. Please note the movement and the time quotient. As soon as torque begins to move it is able to do work, but it is now measurable as horsepower.

The most accurate and generally accepted formula for calculating horsepower is this:

$$Tq \times RPM / 5252 = Hp$$

In this model we see Tq (Torque) Multiplied by RPM (Revolutions Per Minute) and divided by the constant, 5252 equals horsepower. Note this formula addresses those requirements of movement and time within RPM. The element of movement is satisfied by Revolutions and the time quotient by the designation Per minute. Thus both requirements are satisfied by our formula.

Each of these factors must be present to do work and when work is being done it is measured by this mathematical description as horsepower. All of the work done any engine is measurable as horsepower. The mix between torque and RPM that produces horsepower has nothing to do with the ability of the engine to do work.

Let me state this another way. An engine with high torque and low RPM will do no more work than an engine with low torque and high RPM.

Consider a pair of engines. Engine A produces 100 lbs/ft of torque at 6,000 RPM'S and a horsepower of 114.24, according to the formula. Engine B has 200 lbs/ft, double the torque, but turns only 3,000 RPM. Engine B also develops 114.24 horsepower, according to our accepted formula. Our second engine has double the torque but it will do no more work.

The reasons an understanding of this torque/horsepower relationship is so important to the two-stroke aficionado are threefold. First, the two-stroke engine is an RPM engine. It gets the horsepower it develops from high RPM and comparatively low torque output, as in example A. In fact, these figures were taken from a 1989 model, two-stroke engine rated 115 horsepower.

Second, an engine operating with this type of torque/horsepower relationship loses nothing in its ability to do work. How much work it can do will become apparent in the chapter on gears and transmissions. Third, until you understand the nature of the torque/horsepower relationship you will never truly understand the nature of horsepower itself.

High cylinder pressures are needed to generate high torque figures from a short stroke crankshaft. As the rotating speed of the engine increases, the time available to charge the cylinder with a fresh air/fuel mix is decreasing proportionately. If the charge is reduced, the cylinder pressure will also fall off.

A lower cylinder pressure actually means lower torque but as we see above, it does not necessarily mean lower horsepower, if the rpm increases sufficiently. This is the basis for the lightweight, high revving two-stroke. Moderate torque, high RPM, and lots of horsepower are the ruling features of these engines.

CHAPTER FOURTEEN

FLAME PROPAGATION

Perhaps one of the most fascinating subjects you can study is combustion engineering; how things burn and why. Manufacturers of heating appliances, explosives, and combustion engines are all interested in this subject. This is a particularly appropriate area for the two-stroke mechanic since combustion engineering is the basis of flame propagation.

Any piston engine runs on a controlled explosion. The explosion is necessary to the operation of the engine but control is vital. The first diesel engine blew up in the face of its inventor and did serious harm. Consider the elements of flame propagation and control of that explosion in the cylinder.

Flame propagation, as it pertains to the two-stroke engine, is the process by which the fuel/air mix ignites (fires), acquires additional droplets of fuel (propagates), and spreads a flame front across the cylinder. Although this process has been the subject of exhaustive engineering studies, it is possible to put a working model in place, using simple terms.

Begin with a cylinder filled with an air/fuel mix. The spark plug fires and a flame front begins at the point of the spark plug tip. This flame front will spread (propagate) across the face of the piston, involving additional droplets of fuel in the process.

If the temperature and pressure on the fuel is within acceptable limits, the progress or propagation of the flame front will occur in a smooth and orderly manner. This is the best of all worlds. The engines operates smoothly.

Pressure on the piston top is even and well distributed, the cylinder will have no hot spots and will provide a steady push to the piston. The engine runs well and the parts are not overly stressed.

Consider the consequences if pressures or temperatures become excessive. The spark plug ignites the air/fuel charge and the fuel begins to burn. The flame front spreads much more rapidly because of the increased burn rate. The fast moving flame front is driving a high pressure wave before it.

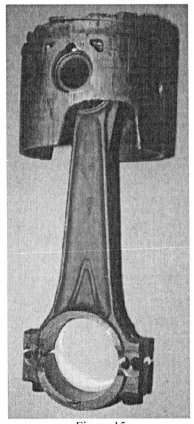

Figure 15

Deteriorated piston top.

The spreading high pressure wave is building a secondary pressure zone near the walls of the cylinder.

Since fuel is distributed throughout the cylinder, the fuel near the walls is subjected to the effects of this spreading high pressure wave.

Pressure creates heat. If you are working around an air compressor, you will find the cylinder head is hot even though there is no fire in the cylinder. This same heat, occurs when any gas is compressed and the higher the pressure, the greater the heat.

If the pressures or temperatures exerted on those remote fuel droplets rises too rapidly they will ignite. There will be a secondary explosion created near the edge of the piston and against the cylinder walls. We call this explosion detonation. It is the sound sometimes described as pinging but it is a very destructive force.

With the advent of that secondary explosion, we lose control of the flame front. The spread no longer occurs in an orderly manner and the burn rate of the fuel occurs at a breakneck pace. Now we have the makings of a full blown disaster.

Burn rate. All explosives have a burn rate. The burn rate of any explosive decides the intensity of the explosion which occurs when that material is ignited. Atomized gasoline is truly an explosive.

The intensity of the explosion created by igniting gasoline within a closed cylinder varies with the heat and pressure which occurs during the time it is burning. The growth or increase of that pressure must surely be greater in a closed environment than it would be in the open air.

If the engine is overloaded, pressure on the piston will be very high and the burn rate of the fuel will increase exponentially. If the air/fuel mixture is too lean the fuel will burn very rapidly and the temperatures will rise accordingly. This elevated temperature reach a magnitude that melts pistons, sticks piston rings, and generally wreaks havoc.

If the ignition timing is too early, the engine fires while

the piston is still well below top dead center. The piston continues to rise against a growing pressure, the burn rate increases and the control of the flame front is lost. All of these conditions can destroy pistons, rings, cylinder bores, and entire engines.

Figure 16

The damaged area of the cylinder head matches that of the previously shown piston.

Our culprits are high ignition timing, an overloaded engine, overly lean mixtures, fuel with an improper octane rating, and in fact anything that interferes with the proper burn rate. I hope that this next concept will clarify, rather than confuse the issue. I am going to offer you a comparison -- the rifle to the engine.

The rifle has a cylinder (bore) just as the engine does. The rifle has a mechanical trigger for its primer while the engine has an electronic trigger for its spark plug. The rifle uses a propellant (powder) to drive its projectile (bullet). The engine uses a propellant (gasoline) to drive its projectile (piston).

The propellant in the rifle has a controlled number of coated grains to retard combustion and it is described as a progressive burning powder. It has a number which tells us how fast it will burn at a given heat and pressure. Powder grains in the rifle cartridge are coated to retard combustion and to control the rate at which new grains are involved in the combustion process.

The engine has a controlled number of droplets in the air/fuel mix. These droplets have a chemical agent to retard the rate at which they burn. The fuel has a number (octane) which describes the rate at which it will burn under any given heat and temperature. In bygone years we used Tetra-Ethyl Lead but today we use a variety of other chemicals.

When you pull the trigger on the rifle and the powder begins to burn, the heat and pressure in the bore will decide if the projectile gets a nice even push or an uncontrolled explosion. If the projectile is too heavy or the propellant charge too great, the rifle will explode.

When the spark plug in the engine fires the charge in the cylinder, the heat and pressure in the bores will decide whether the piston gets a nice even push or a terrible blow. Excessive pressure can cause the rifle to blow up, with disastrous results. The piston is aimed at the crankshaft and rods. If it is loaded with excessive heat and pressure, it too can create drastic results.

Believe it or not, the kinetics, physics and results are amazingly similar. What part does the octane rating of a gasoline have to do with engine performance? That it a nettlesome question but think of it this way: the burn rate of gasoline, like the burn rate of propellant powder, is everything.

An 87 Octane fuel will burn in the engine at the perfect rate if the heat and the pressure in the cylinder match the fuel. So long as this match exists, the 87 octane fuel is as good as any. It contains just as many BTU's of heat energy and it will produce as much power.

Put a fuel with a higher octane rating into the same engine and the fuel will burn too slowly, power will inevitably be lost. Low pressure engines running a high octane fuel often generate very high exhaust temperatures as unburned fuel piles up in the pipe. High octane ratings do not guarantee high horsepower.

Alternatively, if the heat and pressure on the cylinder of

the engine require a fuel with a higher octane rating, then you must use the fuel which that heat or pressure demands. Low octane fuels cannot accept high heat and pressure. Either way, failure to use the proper fuel may cause serious damage to the engine.

Again, we must balance all of the functions of the power plant. The burn rate of our fuel is controlled by heat and pressure. The requirements of the engine dictate the proper octane rating. A fuel that does not balance the needs of the engine will never give satisfactory service.

How does the question of the cross port cylinder versus the loop charged cylinder enter into this? It has to do with the shape and position of the fuel charge in the cylinder.

The cross port engine takes the air/fuel charge into the cylinder through a single set of intake ports on one side and exhausts the burned gasses through another single set of exhaust ports on the opposite side.

The piston has a steep dome, or deflector, on the crown to deflect the incoming charge upward and into the combustion chamber. The shape of that incoming charge is subject to little control and it can only be deflected upward. There is only a limited opportunity to shape the intake for even distribution.

Combustion chamber shapes are also dictated to a large degree by this deflector head on the piston. The combustion chamber shapes designed to control the spread of the flame front are similarly limited. This engine tends to lose a good deal of the incoming charge through the exhaust ports at low speeds and it is an inherently dirty engine for this reason.

As RPM increase and the tuned pipe assumes control of the breathing process, this engine gains greater efficiency, but only through a narrow RPM band where the pipe resonates in phase. At very low speeds it tends to idle quite well, even though it uses a great deal of fuel.

The loop charged engine uses a twin set of intake ports on opposite sides of the cylinder. The charges entering through these opposing ports are largely retained within the cylinder by this opposition. The exhaust is on the third side of the cylinder and less likely to bleed off the incoming charge.

The piston in the loop charge engine may be flat on top or it may have any one of a series of shapes on its surface. It needs no deflector head. Creative efforts are made to incorporate various shapes into the combustion chamber of this engine. The shape of the ports and the resulting loop can be used to help control the spread of the flame front.

Which of these systems is the better one? The loop charged engine is the dominant design today and few cross port engines are being manufactured. The problem of fuel loss out of the open port appears to doom this design. To my knowledge, no cross port engine has ever been run with the new DFI systems which inject fuel into the closed chamber.

A DFI injector might breathe new life into one of these old dogs but the manufacturers seem well satisfied with the looper. It is generally conceded the looper makes a stronger and more powerful engine than does the cross port.

I remember a few times when the two were involved in head-to-head competition on a hydroplane. The loop charged engine usually won those contests but there were times when Lady Luck and a bit of nitro-methane (perfectly legal) tipped the balance in favor of the old cross port. That may be nostalgia talking instead of practicality. For now, bet on the loop charged engine.

CHAPTER FIFTEEN

MECHANICS OF TWO-STROKE ENGINES

In this chapter I will approach the physical and mechanical operations of the engine. You will see the elements of power production and a few mathematical representations to help explain this. The engine is a mechanical device that turns pressure into motion and we are going to explore the ways in which it does this.

I want to begin with a burning gas on top of the piston. This gas applies pressure to the piston top and that pressure is measurable in pounds per square inch. This measurement is usually written lbs/in². Multiply the lbs/in² x the total number of square inches on the piston's surface and you will get the total amount of pressure on the piston.

To make this calculation we need two simple formula. The first will give the number of square inches of piston area.

A (Area) = Pi (3.1416) x R² (Radius)

For the purpose of this demonstration, let us assume the engine has a bore of 3.5 inches. Half of this number is the radius or 1.75 inches. Square that figure (1.75 x 1.75) and we get 3.0625.

Now multiply 3.0625 by 3.1416 and we find the surface of the piston is 9.621 inches. We now have the surface area in square inches for the piston top. We must calculate total pressure. Use this simple formula:

P (Pressure in lbs/in²) x Sq. In. (Square inches of piston surface) = Tp (total pressure)

For this calculation, let us assume a pressure of 150 lbs/in² Now we have P = 150 x 9.621 = 1443.173 total pounds of pressure.

This pressure is pushing down on the connecting rod and that rod will transfer pressure to the crankshaft. Remember, the crankshaft has an arm that actually constitutes a lever. Pressure on that lever will create torque.

How much torque will we have? Let us use a short stroke engine for this demonstration since two-stroke engines lean in that direction. Assume our engine has a stroke of 3 inches. Since the stroke is comprised of piston travel both up and down, the crankshaft arm is equal to one half of the stroke. Thus the arm or lever on the crankshaft is equal to 1.5 inches.

Torque is measured in foot pounds, based upon the assumption of a 1 foot lever, but our lever is only a fraction of a foot in length. We have to convert that 1.5 inch arm to feet. Dividing 12 inches into 1.5 inches we find the arm is .125 feet in length. We have 1442.173 lbs/in² of pressure applied to the .125 foot lever. That will yield 180.2716 Lbs./Ft. of torque (.125 x 1442.173).

This is not exactly accurate, for reasons I will discuss shortly, but the principal is good and the mathematics sound. Why is the torque produced not an exact result of pressure on the crankshaft arm? It would be if we had all that pressure from the piston top pushing downward in a straight line.

Unfortunately, there is a matter of angle between the direction of the force applied by the piston and the crankshaft arm. The connecting rod joins the crankshaft arm at an ever changing angle and the percentage of pressure delivered from the piston top to the crankshaft arm varies in proportion to that angle. There is always a loss involved.

What I really want you to learn from all this is we have

pressure applied to the piston. The results can be calculated exactly. The pressure will be applied to the crankshaft arm and torque will result. Torque is much more difficult to calculate.

The calculation involves a resolution of forces diagram which resolves the effect of forces applied in indirect lineage. Since the angle of the crankshaft arm, relative to the connecting rod, changes with every degree of crankshaft travel, a new calculation would be required for every degree of crankshaft travel.

Computer models do this work today and resolution of forces diagrams are outside the scope of this book. It is desirable to understand the manner in which cylinder pressure becomes torque.

If the cylinder pressure remains constant, we can increase either of the two factors, bore or stroke, and the result will be more torque and more horsepower. If the cylinder pressure remains constant, we can increase the RPM and the horsepower alone will increase proportionately.

The RPM alone does not effect the amount of developed torque If the cylinder pressure remains constant. The problem lies in the fact that the engine will, at some point, breathe out.

Every engine has an RPM limit beyond which it cannot fully charge the cylinder with air/fuel mix. When that point is reached, the cylinder pressure will begin to fall and the total pressure on the piston top will be reduced. Now the torque also begins to fall. Why does the pressure fall off?

The charging of the cylinder is measured as volumetric efficiency. It takes into consideration the amount of pressure in the air, 14.7 pounds per square inch, at sea level. It then considers the amount of pressure present in the cylinder when the last port closes.

The percentage of that 14.7 pound atmospheric pressure that enters the cylinder, in the time allowed by the rotating speed of the engine, is also the percentage of volumetric efficiency the engine achieves. The volumetric efficiency of the engine is dependent on many design factors:

port size, pipe tuning, reed valve areas, and a host of other factors.

This percentage will always be less than 100 and as the RPM increase, the volumetric efficiency will reach a point then begin to fall. The outside air pressure is simply not enough to drive a full charge of air/fuel mix into the cylinder, in the time available.

Will the horsepower also fall? Not yet. Horsepower will eventually fall, but it will actually increase as the RPM increases for a time. The developed torque is falling off, yet the ability of the engine to do useful work is still increasing. It will only do this for a limited time.

How can we get more horsepower as we are losing torque?

Go to any engine dealer. Ask him for a torque and horsepower curve for any engine. The principals will be the same for all engines. Look at the curve and you will see a very graphic illustration of the stated principals. The RPM are on the horizontal or "Y" axis while torque, horsepower, or both, are on the vertical or "X" axis.

Looking at the curve, you will notice both torque and horsepower increase as the RPM increase. At this point cylinder pressure is also on the increase.

After the midrange speed of the engine, the torque curve will first peak and then begin to fall. The engine is running out of breath and the pressure on the piston top is less than before. Yet the horsepower curve continues to rise. How can this be? Remember that horsepower is a product of both TORQUE and RPM.

As long as the RPM rises faster than the developed torque falls, the engine will continue to make more horsepower. When the cylinder pressure, and consequently the developed torque, fall too fast, the engine will reach a peak in horsepower, then the horsepower will begin to fall as well.

For your knowledge, the torque peak is the point the engine is most efficient and economical. The horsepower peak is the point the engine produces the greatest amount of work (horsepower) and should be at maximum RPM.

The proper propeller on an engine will allow the engine to turn at the RPM speed where the horsepower peaks, no more. Any fewer RPM and the engine is overloaded. Higher RPM, the engine is spinning free, losing power, wasting fuel, and overworking the internal parts. Let us look at a slightly different approach.

The formula we have been using is the most accurate to calculate horsepower. It gives a better picture of the engines ability to do work.

The next formula we will employ gives the amount of power developed within the engine's cylinders and does not take into account certain friction losses, etc. Yet it does offer a great model for description and understanding of certain processes.

$$P \times L \times A \times N / 33,000 = HP$$

In this model, P is the average pressure on the tops of the pistons during combustion; "L" is the length of the stroke, expressed in feet, or fractions thereof; "A" is the area of the tops of all the pistons, in square inches; "N" is the number of power strokes in each minute. This formula contains every one of those principals we have been concerned with.

The area of the piston tops, the pressure thereon, the length of the stroke, expressed in feet, and the number of power strokes in each minute.

On a two-stroke engine, the number of revolutions per minute will be the same as the number of power strokes. The RPM of the four-stroke must be divided by two to get the number of power strokes in each minute since the four-stroke only fires every other revolution.

If the two-stroke fires twice as often as the four-stroke for a given number of revolutions, it still wil not produce twice the horsepower. The reason for this lies in the first factor in our equation, P for cylinder pressure. The four-stroke can produce greater cylinder pressures than a two-stroke provides and it makes up a bit of ground in the pressure differential.

The last of these formulae, are the calculations of compression ratio and compression pressure. First, what is the compression ratio? This is the numerical relationship between the total number of cubic inches above the piston when it rests at bottom dead center and the total number of cubic inches above the piston when it rests at top dead center.

This is easier than it sounds. Run the piston down and measure the space above it. Let us assume 100 cubic inches for this discussion. Run the piston to the top and measure the remaining space. Let us assume 15 cubic inches for this illustration.

In this formula, substitute ratio and proportion, 100:15:X:I. Here we see 15X = 100 and X = 6.666 or a 6.67:1 compression ratio. This is a theoretical compression ratio since the engine does not begin to build pressure until the last valve or port closes. This is also the figure you are given in engine literature.

In the next chapter we will consider engine design and explore the actual compression ratio. View the engine's operation and add the function of flame propagation. Try to see the first red flare of the flame as the air/fuel mix is set to burning. Think about the spread of that flame across the piston top and visualize the shock wave racing before it. The speed of that wave and the temperature that it generates will decide the fate of our engine.

Consider the fuel itself. Hundreds of small droplets are being progressively involved in the burning process. Will the pressure wave remain under control? Will the cylinder temperature remain within acceptable limits? Can we expect that moving flame front to travel all the way to the cylinder walls in an orderly fashion? If they do, our engine will run well.

If you have torn the engine down for inspection and find a white ring around the piston top at the edge of the cylinder, the carbon is burned away. This is a sign of early detonation. If you see the edges of the piston eroded and scars in the bores, the engine is in the advanced stages of detonation.

It is very difficult to imagine all of these events that must occur in exact sequence, so many parts moving together in exact time, a mechanical symphony of steel and aluminum. Imagine so much technology in motion, but after all, this is an engine. The engine is one of the most exciting and powerful contrivances which man has yet devised.

CHAPTER SIXTEEN

ENGINE DESIGN

This chapter will be about as much fun as any in the entire book. We are going to look at the dimensions of the engine and how they can be switched around to produce a desired mix of torque, horsepower, and RPM. The material will help you choose an engine for any given application. It will help you understand qualities of engine longevity and speed.

There are a few things you should consider about two-stroke outboards. They're intended to be light, maneuverable, easily mounted and removed, and in many cases portable. They must furnish substantial horsepower to boats that cannot utilize heavy engines.

With those design parameters in mind, you will understand this is also a specialized engine for diverse, yet limited applications.

Make no mistake about it, speed (high RPM) and longevity do not go together. Yet high RPM performance is where we get our extended horsepower capabilities without great weight. So the engine becomes a compromise. We employ a reasonable mix of the two to get an engine that will produce substantial power, from small displacement, and yet live for a reasonable life span

For this illustration let us create a mythical engine. Call it *Super Gizmo*. This engine has a bore of 3.5 inches and a stroke of 3.0 inches. This is a reasonable model for an outboard, two-stroke engine. What is the significance of this bore/stroke selection?

An engine with a bore and stroke of the same dimensions is said to be a square engine. If the bore is greater than the stroke the engine is over square. If the bore is less than the stroke the engine is said to be under square. Obviously, Super Gizmo is an over square engine.

The relationship between bore and stroke is expressed as a percentage and is said to be the bore/stroke ratio. Engines with bore/stroke ratios above 1.00 are under square. They tend to have long arms on the crankshaft and they develop higher torque figures.

Engines with bore/stroke ratios below 1.00 are over square engines. They develop less torque than their long-legged brethren and get their horsepower from higher RPM. How about Super Gizmo?

Dividing the 3.5 inch bore into the 3.00 inch stroke, we find Super Gizmo has a bore/stroke ratio of 0.8571. This is an RPM engine and that short arm on the crankshaft will not develop large amounts of low end torque. We have to turn this to get the horsepower.

Let us consider a V-6 cylinder configuration for Super Gizmo. This gives us a total of 173.093 cubic inches. Mathematically calculated using a well respected formula.

$$B \times B \times S \times .785 \times N = D$$

In this formula Bore (3.50) x Bore (3.50) x stroke (3.00) x .785 x the Number of cylinders (6) = Cubic inches (173.0925).

Cubic displacement is the basis on which all engines are compared. Racing engines all fall into classes governed by cubic displacement. We will look at changes with and without the limits of that 173 cubic inches which Super Gizmo has to offer.

Let us give Super Gizmo a horsepower output of 225 at 6,000 RPM. Now see what changes we might make to this engine and how they will effect its performance. While we think about changes, let us also think about that horsepower formula we just finished:

$$P \times L \times A \times N / 33{,}000 = HP$$

First, how we can change the horsepower or developed torque in this engine. Increase any one of the first three factors in the equation and we will increase torque. Those three are: cylinder pressure, length of the crankshaft arm, and area of the piston tops. Increase any one of the factors in the top half of the formula and we will increase horsepower. Let us start with the P for pressure.

There are several ways to increase cylinder pressure. We can raise the compression ratio but if we do we will probably need a higher octane for the gasoline. We can open the ports and the carburetor venturis and let in more air. Maybe, but we may lose some low end performance if we do. Our idle will surely suffer and we may well increase the fuel consumption.

How about "L", the length of the crankshaft arm? That will get us some more torque and horsepower too. At least it will at low RPM. Why only at low RPM and not high RPM as well? There is a price to be paid as the speed (RPM) increases. We have to consider kinetics in any design. Kinetics or kinetic energy is a kind of energy that appends to all moving objects which have mass (weight).

The formula for the calculation of kinetic energy. Is KE $= MV^2$. This formula tells us that Kinetic Energy is equal to the Mass (in this case piston weight) multiplied by the square of the velocity (piston speed). As the piston speed increases, the kinetic energy in that piston increases geometrically (as the square of the velocity).

We have a missile flying around in the cylinder and it gets much stronger as the speed increases. Add to that problem, we have to absorb that energy and it is then lost. The more energy we must absorb, the greater the loss.

There are about 5 degrees of dead crankshaft travel at

both the top and the bottom of the stroke. During these times the piston is not moving. You have to stop the piston at the top of the stroke and start it moving again. You must also stop the piston at the bottom of the stroke and start it moving again. There will be two starts and two stops for every revolution. A lot of energy loss occurs here.

In the short stroke, high RPM engine we have less torque and less piston speed. This requires much less energy to make those stops at top dead center and at bottom dead center. In the long stroke, high torque engine we develop much higher piston speeds, if the RPM remains constant. The kinetic energy is greater and requires a lot more energy to make those same starts and stops, if the RPM remain constant for both engines. With a longer stoke, we will actually gain both torque and horsepower at low RPM when piston speeds are still minimal. As the RPM increase, the kinetic energy loss will grow exponentially.

The advantage in both torque and horsepower will disappear but the engine wear will grow dramatically. It does this because the piston speeds are much higher for a given RPM increment and the rings are going to wear to a greater degree. Calculate piston speed using this formula:

$$S \times 2 \times R / 12 = Ps$$

We see S is the Stroke (3.00 inches) x 2 x Revolutions Per Minute (6,000), divided by 12 equals piston speed in feet per minute. The piston speed on this engine is 3,000 feet per minute. Remember that comparison we made earlier between a rifle and an engine?

That piston is already traveling at a speed greater than a .30-06 caliber rifle bullet and we have to start it and stop it twice, during every revolution. It would be nice to have the longer stroke but we do not need more piston speed? Let us cut the RPM instead. We can do that but then we will gain little or no horsepower. The engine would have to employ a greater deck height. This is the height of the block above the crankshaft centerline. To accommodate the longer stroke, we would need more room in the crankcase and the connecting rod would be longer. We are rapidly gaining weight and this could be a real problem. Try another part of the formula, R.

Why don't we just turn the engine faster? Okay, now the piston speeds begin to increase again. The kinetic loads increase and both bearing and piston wear will increase. Did you have to open up the venturi of the carburetor to get the extra air/fuel mix for this increase in operating speed? How about the ports. Did you have to raise them to let in more air/fuel mix?

Congratulations, you have shortened the power stroke by opening the ports early and you have slowed the flow of fuel in the intake passages at low speed. How much bottom end (low RPM performance) did you have to give up to get this increase in speed?

What we are seeing here is a very real set of tradeoffs and the engineers who designed that engine did so with an eye for balance. They began with an objective, to produce an engine which would provide the best possible mix of size, weight, bore, stroke, torque and RPM to do a specific job. To understand this process will help the boater in several ways.

First, it will help you to understand the engine w you may buy or now own. You know that the engine must have a longer stroke if it is to develop greater torque. You know the longer stroke causes faster ring wear and plays hob with the kinetics. You know a bigger bore gives more room for larger ports to breathe the engine but it also increases piston weight and to a smaller degree, increases kinetics.

In the future you should be better able to select that one engine is right for your own purposes and do so on a scientific basis.

You should also realize the mix of dimensions were selected for the various engines offered today are close to optimum for there purpose.

We have now explored the operation of the power head, thoroughly. Let us move on to the lower unit and see how power at the top of the outboard engine is transmitted to a propeller.

CHAPTER SEVENTEEN

PAN, COWL & DRIVE SHAFT HOUSING

The pan and cowl are very important to the engine. The pan is an aluminum casting. It is flat in the center and curled at the edges, thus it has a shape not unlike a pan. The pan has a hole in the center which is shaped like the hole in the power head and permits the emergence of cooling water and exhaust gas.

There are holes in the pan to accommodate the bolts which attach the power head to the drive shaft housing and gaskets are fitted to each side to seal the gasses and cooling water inside. Bolts pass through the pan and secure the three, power head, pan and drive shaft housing together.

A two-way switch which operates the tilt/trim motor is mounted inside the pan with wires emerging from the switch to connect it to the tilt/trim system. There is an opening in the front portion of the pan to accommodate the electric control cable and the throttle/shift controls for the engine.

Enlarged portions of the pan allow for the bolting on of mounting parts for the various cables. The fuel inlet connection is also bolted to this pan. There are any one of several different styles of attachment toggles or levers which hold the cowling on top of this pan.

A pan seal is a rubber grommet which encircles the top of the pan and it is intended to seal against the lower edge of the cowling. The pan is an important part of five different things. It is needed to hold the cowling, accept and anchor the controls, to facilitate sound deadening for the engine, it seals against the intrusion of water from wind and wave, it is an important part of the engine's shape and styling.

The cowling is generally laid up from several layers of fiberglass. It must be strong and as a result, it is comparatively heavy. This weight also adds to its usefulness for sound deadening. The cowling must seal to the pan at the bottom. It has holes in its upper portion to admit air for the engine's operation.

The manufacturers logo and selected graphics decorate the sides, back, and front of the cowling. The shape and styling of the engine are expressed more completely here than in any other part of the engine. Lately more attention has been given to compactness and to aerodynamic shapes. As engines got heavier, an effort was made to keep them from looking clumsy or unwieldy.

There will be plastic covered sound deadening attached to the inside areas of the cowling. Clamps from the pan grab special brackets in the cowling, for attachment.

The drive shaft housing hardly seems to rate more than a line in a chapter, let alone a chapter in a book. Oddly enough, that is not the case. The drive shaft housing is the unheralded and forgotten servant that quietly does many things.

This housing is cast of aluminum and it has webbing at top and bottom for bolt holes. These holes are used to mount the power head above and the gear case below . It is both the structure that holds the engine together and the skeleton to which the mounting bracket is bolted.

The mounting bracket may have a C-clamp shape or it may simply be flat across the face. If the mounting bracket has the C-clamp shape it also has mounting screws to attach the engine to the vessel. These screws have a toggle handle on one end for tightening the screw and a washer on the other end to protect and grip the transom of the boat. These screws should be firmly clamped at all times.

Engines with this arrangement are usually considered portable engines; 15 horsepower or less. If the engine is left on the boat, the mounting screws should be checked before every use. If the engine is removed and replaced at every use, the operator should be certain they are tight before operating the engine.

Larger engines; 25 to 35 horsepower, may have the C-clamp mounting system also. Below the C-clamp there will be a hole on each side of the bracket for the very important safety bolts. Holes must be drilled through the transom of the vessel. This may seem to be a bit excessive, but it is not.

Those safety bolts are a deterrent to theft but they are also important to the safety of the operator. Engines that can attain speeds of 25 miles per hour, or more, are very likely to come loose from the transom under impact. They may also climb into the boat with an unsuspecting operator. Always install those safety bolts.

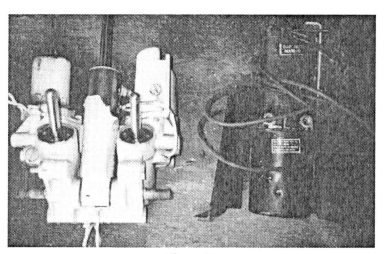

Figure 17

Power trim and tilt unit.

Larger engines have only bolt holes through the mounting bracket. The engine is through bolted to the transom with four stout bolts. The bracket is strong aluminum. The tilt/trim mechanism is mounted inside this bracket. A hydraulic cylinder with an electric motor to power the system is located here.

The tilt/trim motor is a two-way motor that can run in either direction. A switch to activate the tilt/trim motor is located on the side of the engine cowling and another on the remote control lever. On a bass boat there may be a third switch at the bow so the angler can tilt the engine without leaving the seat.

These are two-way, toggle switches which can energize the field in the motor for rotation in either direction, Up or Down.

The drive shaft housing dictates the length the engine. The housing is measured from the bottom side of the bracket where it sits on the transom to the top of the anti-cavitation plate. A housing with a 15 inch dimension is a standard housing. Housings with a 20 inch dimension are long shafts while those with a 25 inch measurement are extra long. A few engines have a 30 inch drive shaft housing and they are described as extra, extra long.

The foregoing are proper descriptions and they are accepted by all manufacturers. If you use the verbal descriptions you will find many boaters and an unacceptable number of mechanics are confused about the nomenclature.

There are a number of drive shaft housings that are designed for special application racing engines. They vary in length from engine to engine and from manufacturer to manufacturer. These housings are describe by various terms such as Hydro-short and there is no norm for their length. The lengths vary around 10-1/2 inches to 11- 1/2 inches.

I will not try to detail all of these units. That is outside the scope of this book but they do exist. I will touch briefly upon their use in Chapter Eighteen for the same reason. It is easy to see that there are many selections available to the boater and just as easy to understand the potential for confusion.

I would suggest you stay with the actual measurements in any negotiation of an engine or boat you intend to match up yourself. Manufacturers and dealers use the actual lengths for orders and discussions.

The drive shaft housing also encloses that tuned exhaust pipe. The pipe is usually bolted to the power head at the top end and opens at the lower end of the housing. Depending upon the state of tune, the pipe may be open inside the housing or grommeted to an outlet which funnels the exhaust to the propeller under full control.

Cooling water from the power head is discharged through the drive shaft housing. The housing is water cooled and in many cases uses water flow to help as a sound shield. Cooling water also keeps heat off the gaskets, grommets, and other parts which can easily be damaged by heat.

I realize many owners of outboard engines will ignore this paragraph. I see the coming advice violated every day, and many boaters become angry if you mention it to them. Never, ever, crank an outboard engine without a good and sufficient water supply available to the engine. Not even for just a minute!

The water pump impeller is susceptible to friction and it drags the case of the water pump housing at all times. The only lubrication it has is the water it pumps. Run it dry and it will heat up immediately. The pump will surely be damaged.

Those gaskets and grommets inside the drive shaft housing do not like heat. The hot exhaust, is traveling through the drive shaft housing, heating up the housing and destroying everything that is not a metal part. If you do not see a discharge from the telltale hole at the side of the engine cowling, shut it down immediately.

There are sacrificial anodes attached to the drive shaft housing. They are important if the engine is to be operated in saltwater. Saltwater is an electrolyte and electrolysis will destroy the engine if these zincs are not maintained. Electrolysis attacks any dissimilar metals immersed in its presence and there are many stainless steel fittings on the mounting bracket.

There are also ferrous metals in the tilt/trim motor housing. Stainless steel propellers are a large source of trouble in saltwater. No, the stainless steel is not going to give up electrons in the electrolytic process but the aluminum drive shaft housing will.

There is a scale which rates metals for nobility. Nobility is the tendency to give up free electrons in the electrolytic process. The more noble the metal, the more easily it gives up free electrons. Aluminum is more noble than stainless steel, thus very vulnerable when both are immersed together.

Zinc is a highly noble metal and is higher on the scale than either aluminum or stainless steel. Thus the anodes are made of zinc. The zinc will deteriorate before either aluminum or stainless steel parts. The zinc anode is sacrificed to save those expensive engine parts.

Inspect the zincs carefully. When they are 25 percent gone, they are no longer effective. Replace them immediately. Failure to do so may produce results that are not visible but destructive. There is one alternative to the zinc anode that is worth mentioning. I do not generally refer to a specific product from a particular company but Mercury Marine manufactures the only active cathodic protection that I am aware of.

The Merc-Cathode is a reverse polarity generator that reverses the flow of electrons and nullifies the effects of electrolysis. A potentiometer in the line reads the amount of current flow and indicates the direction of that flow on a gauge. The electron flow is controllable and electrolysis can be held in suspension with this device.

The aluminum alloys of the drive shaft housings are the subject of endless research and development. Aluminum and copper are the most prevalent metals with other trace metals for strength. The drive shaft housing is continuously tested in corrosion testing facilities that are guarded like the doors to Fort Knox.

Indeed, it may be easier to get in to see the national treasury than to get into the Mercury corrosion testing facility at Placida, Florida. The alloys which emerge from these testing programs are given exotic names. Advertising which is incomprehensible to the public and little understood by those who write the ads often makes its way into print.

Be assured of one thing: You will not engineer away electrolysis. You can only accommodate the problem and the zinc anode is the only effective system for the purpose. Ignore it at your peril.

CHAPTER EIGHTEEN

THE GEAR CASE

The gear case on the outboard engine is in fact a transmission and it has all of the attributes. It has forward-neutral-reverse direction changes and a set of gears for changing the relationship between engine speed and propeller speed. We call this a reduction gear and it is vital to the satisfactory operation of the two-stroke engine.

The outboard gear case may turn either, left hand or right hand. The reason for this arrangement is to permit counter rotating pairs or matched engines which rotate in opposite directions. This counters the torque from a single propeller and cancels out drift which is a side to side movement caused by propeller torque.

First let us examine the parts of the gear case. Virtually every outboard uses the same general system and the same parts break down, though the design of those parts will be different. We begin with a gear case which is cast of aluminum. An anti-cavitation plate is spread around the top of the case. There are two shafts, one drive shaft and one propeller shaft for the system.

The drive shaft enters the gear case from the top while the propeller shaft exits the case at the aft (rear) end. The water pump housing is mounted on top of the gear case and the propeller shaft penetrates this housing, passing through it as it enters the gear case. There is a neoprene seal below the water pump to keep grease in the housing and water out.

A rubber or neoprene impeller sits inside the water pump housing and it is keyed to the drive shaft. Thus, the impeller turns at the same speed as the engine, in gear or out of gear. This is necessary to prevent engine overheat during idle operation.

The water pump housing is gasketed onto the top of the gear case and mounted with several screws. It furnishes water to the engine through a copper tube that runs from the water pump housing, upward to the cylinder block. Rubber grommets seal this tube at top and bottom.

Figure 18

This gear case cutaway shows the construction of a typical drive.

There is a shift rod or shift shaft that emerges from the top of the gear case and also rises upward to the shifter located on the side of the engine itself. This shaft accomplishes the change of directions from forward to reverse but cannot change the gear ratio.

There are three gears in the case. A pinion (drive) gear, a forward (driven) gear, and a reverse (driven) gear. There is also a clutch dog that makes the direction changes. Bearings at the top of the gear case support the drive shaft and they are usually ball bearings or a combination of ball and needle bearing.

The gears may be straight cut or spiral. Straight cut gears extend outward from the center or hub of the gear in, as a radius of the circle the gear comprises. Spiral gears are spread across the face of the gear in a curved pattern. Each of these shapes has its advantages and disadvantages.

The spiral gear set is very quiet and has little or no gear whine. This gear is not as strong as a straight cut gear. The straight cut gear set has more area of its teeth in contact at any given time and this greater contact area is the source of its strength. Nonetheless, it is noisier than the spiral gear. Almost all modern outboard engines use the straight cut gear.

Though the noise is audible, the straight cut gear is needed for its strength and to preclude the requirement for larger gears. Larger gears would require a larger gear case and consequently produce more drag in the water. The largest problem with the straight cut gear is in a four-stroke outboard where sound is nil at very low speeds.

The engine sits on a boat and you can barely hear the engine run but in many instances, you can hear the gears whine above the engine sound. This destroys the near silence of that very quiet engine. The two-stroke engine has enough noise at idle and the whine is not noticeable.

There is a carrier which fits into the rear end of the gear case and closes off the opening. The carrier, carries the ball and roller bearings that support the propeller shaft. It also holds the seal that keeps grease in the gear case and water out

There is a shifting fork or shifting detent that causes directional changes in the gear case. Mercury Marine tends to use the detent while OMC uses the shifting fork. Others vary in their selection. Both systems work very well and the outboard gear case will generally outlast the engine, if it is properly used and maintained.

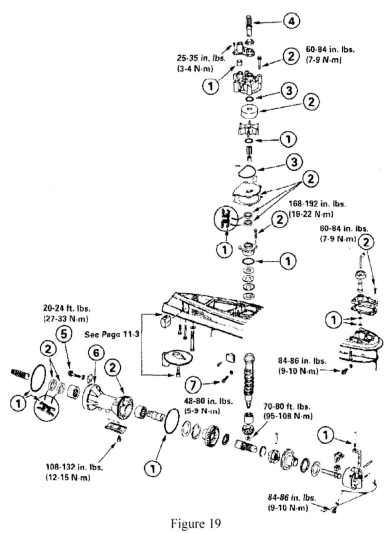

Figure 19
Courtesy of OMC.

Exploded view of an OMC gear case.

The operation of this gear case is an interesting concept. The drive gear or pinion is mounted rigidly on the drive shaft. Both driven gears, forward and reverse, are mounted on the propeller shaft with bearings between shaft and gear. All three gears are in constant mesh and the driven gears are turning in opposite directions on the propeller shaft.

The propeller shaft has a splined area in the center of the shaft and the clutch dog is splined onto the propeller shaft. The dog is loose enough to side back and forth on those splines. It has teeth or a ratchet provision on both sides of the dog which permit it to engage the driven gears, forward or reverse, selectively.

Figure 20

Water pump housing, shift lever and drive shaft.

When the dog is slid backwards or forward it will engage one or the other of the gears on the propeller shaft. The shaft is then locked onto that gear and turns in response to that engagement. The remaining driven gear is now running free but turning in the opposite direction, just the same. This is a neat arrangement. If you're really interested in the way these things work it would be worthwhile to ask a mechanic to show you one.

Because the engines usually share common gear cases

and common propellers for several horsepower ratings it is quite common for a single case to have many different gear ratios. This allows a single gear case to serve more than one engine horsepower and pull larger or smaller propellers than their horsepower ratings would seem to indicate. There are engines with gear ratios as low as 13:39 or 3:1. Then there is the Big Foot gear case.

The Big Foot gear case has a very low gear ratio indeed. It can allow engines of modest horsepower to pull big propellers and heavy loads.

What do we need to know about gear ratios and the two-stroke engine? Well now, let us go back to the time element or the rate at which work is delivered.

Reduction gears are rated in numerical expressions which always give input revolutions first and output revolutions second. Gears with a first number which is greater than the second are considered to be reduction gears. Through these gears the output RPM will be reduced by the amount of the gear ratio but the torque will increase in like proportion.

Gears with the first number smaller than the latter are considered to be over drive gears. They will increase the output RPM in relationship to input RPM. These gears increase propeller shaft RPM and reduce torque.

Remember, gears and pulleys only change the rate at which work is delivered but do not change the total amount of work done. Here is an example: Let us assume we have a one horsepower motor set up to lift 33,000 pounds, one foot, in one minute. We also know it will lift 16,500 pounds, two feet, in one minute or 66,000 pounds, 1/2 foot, in one minute.

We are working with gears or pulleys to change the rate of delivery but not the total amount of work. Levers operate the same way. A long stroke with low force is applied to the lever on one side of the fulcrum or pivot point. A shorter stoke with much greater force results on the other side of the fulcrum.

In effect, we invest a little effort over a great distance to lift a great weight over a lesser distance. The ratio between the length of the lever before and after the fulcrum decides the mechanical advantage. The total amount of work done on each side of the lever remains the same.

The same relationship applies to torque. Take our mythical engine, Super Gizmo, and give it 100 lbs/ft of torque at 6,000 RPM. We know from the formula we have been using that 100 lbs/ft of torque multiplied by 6,000 RPM gives us 600,000, which we divide by the constant 5252 and get 114.242 horsepower.

Suppose we run Super Gizmo through a 2:1 reduction gear. The RPM will be reduced by half, the torque at the output shaft will double and now we have 200 lbs/ft of torque but only 3,000 RPM. Yes, the horsepower is still the same. We can turn a much larger propeller but we can only turn it half as fast.

We could go the other way. We might try a 1:2 gear ratio and turn the propeller twice as fast as the engine turns. If we did this the gear ratio would be 1:2.

Now we will only get 50 lbs/ft of torque and the RPM will be 12,000. Of course, we can only turn a very small propeller and it will have only limited use. How about the horsepower? By now you already know the answer, but. Take 50 lbs/ft of torque, multiply by 12,000 RPM and get 600,000 which we are going to divide by 5252. Yes, the same 114.242 horsepower keeps cropping up in our calculations. The comforting thing about this is, through the use of reduction gears, we are able to pull hefty propellers with an outboard engine having very modest developed torque.

Another valuable trait of this gear system is its ability to allow the engine to turn at its rated RPM under load. For applications such as sailboats where the engine is required to pull large vessels which travel at relatively low speed, this is a blessing. The fouled spark plugs and increased fuel consumption that plagued those overloaded outboard engines, need not be such a problem now.

Of course there are the in-between uses for these engines such as the pontoon boat. This is a platform that makes moderate speed, carries many passengers, and is not generally intended for large two-strokes. Enter the reduction gear. Now a small engine can get the job done, hauling substantial numbers of passengers, turning a larger propeller, through a reduction gear.

A final word to the wise: The stainless steel propeller is heavy and it is the enemy of your clutch dog. The inertia of that heavy propeller, sitting at rest, must be overcome instantly when the clutch dog engages. The engine is turning 850 to 1,000 RPM and the prop shaft about half of that.

The dog engages the gears and there is no give as with a hydraulic clutch. The reaction is instant, wham. You grab that heavy propeller and bring it up to speed in a heartbeat. The gear load on engagement, with a stainless steel propeller, can be three or four times as great as that of an aluminum propeller.

We will take up this phenomenon in the next chapter on set up but I will make it short and sweet: If you do not need a stainless steel propeller, do not use one.

CHAPTER NINETEEN

PROPELLERS

The propeller gurus are well represented in the prop shops of America. A greater number are in the coffee shops and marinas. They know everything about propellers. I know a little about propellers and I can share most of that knowledge with you in a few paragraphs. I hope that you find them worth reading.

I want to begin with a dictionary. Thus, we can have a good understanding of the terms we will use. As we progress, we will also establish a few rules for propeller performance. They may not be exactly what you think.

The propeller has a hub which is the round center section or skeleton. A set of blades or flukes may be cast with the hub, welded onto the hub, or inserted into the hub. In the early years the most common term was fluke. The propeller blades, did in fact resemble the flukes on a whale. The blades on a modern propeller have a vastly different shape.

The propeller hub may be solid or it may have a slip clutch. The solid hub may have a shear pin or it may be splined onto the propeller shaft. The solid hub designed for use with a shear pin has a hole in the propeller hub and a corresponding hole in the propeller shaft.

The shear pin itself, is a cylindrical pin made of soft metal. It passes through both sets of holes, those in the propeller and those in the propeller shaft. It is held in tension by the propeller nut. This pin shears on impact to protect the propeller shaft and propeller. The shear pin must then be replaced.

There are other propellers with no impact protection whatsoever. The solid hub propeller is an example. It has no shear pin and no slip clutch. It is useful for limited purposes but dangerous during operation. Any collision between a solid hub propeller and a foreign object usually destroys the propeller, the propeller shaft, and everything in the gear case.

This is a special purpose propeller, designed for large engines of high horsepower, and intended for use on a race course only. It should not be used for general operation. It is designed to accept the terrible torque forces that occur when the propeller becomes momentarily airborne and then reenters the water. That brings us to the splined hub with a slip clutch.

By far the most common propeller in use today employs the rubber-cored slip hub. It is splined onto the propeller shaft and slips on impact. If the slippage is severe, the hub will be freed from the spline and the propeller will must be rehubbed. This operation can only be undertaken by an experienced propeller shop.

Figure 21
Courtesy of Piranha.

Plastic prop with replaceable blades.

Propellers are commonly made of aluminum, bronze, stainless steel or a plastic composite. Aluminum propellers are the most prevalent, followed by stainless steel. Few bronze propellers are on outboards but there are some excellent plastic composite propellers in use.

Plastic propellers, with inserted blades, are manufactured under the name Piranha. The extensive tests I have run on these propellers, show excellent impact resistance, and simple repairs with little or no damage to the engine, from the impact.

The basic measurements of the propeller are diameter and pitch. The diameter of the propeller is the same as the diameter of a circle comprised by the outside tips of the blades. The pitch is the distance the propeller would travel through the water in one revolution, if there were no slip.

Propellers with relatively large diameter and low pitch are considered to be load props or work props. Propellers with relatively low diameter and higher pitch are considered to be speed props. Propellers in the middle of the spectrum are considered to be general purpose props.

The propeller for a two-stroke engine is very efficient in forward gear yet it offers little in reverse. This effect is achieved by design. There is no way to get the enviable amount of thrust produced by a two-stroke propeller in both directions.

The propeller designers opted for an imbalance towards forward operation. This is a fine decision until you try to stop your outboard powered houseboat in a following sea or a tail wind. Then things may get a bit sticky. This entire system is another of those compromises that seem to work very well-- most of the time.

Both the diameter and the pitch of all propellers is given in inches not degrees. Diameter is an exact measurement while the pitch of the propeller is somewhat less exact. Every propeller, today is a progressive pitch propeller. It has a different pitch at the hub than that at the tips of the blades. This fact alone leads to much controversy.

The rate the pitch progresses from hub to tip is often

referred to as the rate of twist. This rate varies widely from manufacturer to manufacturer. It is this factor, more than any other, which leads to an inexact description of the qualities of a propeller. The pitch of the blade is measured by a Pitch-O-Meter.

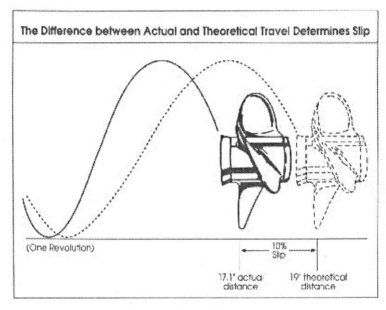

The Difference between Actual and Theoretical Travel Determines Slip

(One Revolution)

10% Slip

17.1" actual distance   19" theoretical distance

Figure 22

The Pitch-O-Meter measures the height of the blade surface in a number of places, adds the numbers, and averages the result. The answer is the theoretical pitch that would result from the variable blade shape. To illustrate this effect, lay a straight edge across the blade, in line with the hub. Slide the straight edge back and forth across the blades and watch the angle change. You are seeing the variation in blade angle and the continual change in pitch.

The pitch for any propeller is useful for comparison purposes only. Factory made, aluminum propellers will generally be very consistent but once you enter the world of after market, stainless steel propellers, you are on your own.

They can set the water on fire and give literally unbelievable results or they can be a very costly experiment.

Three other propeller measurements are rake, lift, and cup. The rake in the propeller is measured by the amount of blade that extends behind the hub of the prop. The lift in the propeller is exactly that. The propeller has the ability to lift the bow or the stern of the boat and it is generally designed to do one or the other, to a greater or lesser degree.

The hull may also have lift built in and designed to trim at a specific angle. The mating of hull to propeller must take into account all of the design characteristics of each, if the union is to be successful.

The most controversial feature of the propeller is the cupping of the blades. Cupping the blades of a propeller is a way to reduce slip. Cupping the blade of a propeller does not increase the pitch. It may have the effect of increased pitch since the slip is reduced and the distance the boat travels through the water for each revolution of the propeller is increased.

How about an example? The boat has a propeller with 17 inches of pitch but the propeller is slipping (cavitating) as it turns. The result is that the boat only travels 12 inches through the water for each complete revolution of the blades. So, we cup the blades and the cavitation lessens. The boat now travels 14 inches through the water for each complete revolution of the blades.

The boat is still traveling less than 17 inches for every complete revolution of the blades. We have improved our performance but we have not increased the pitch of the propeller. A propeller with 17 inches of pitch will never travel more than 17 inches across the water for each complete revolution of the blades, regardless of how much it is cupped

The next concept is the propeller as a governor. The first measure of proper propeller selection is this: It must keep the engine turning within the factory rated RPM range, with the load it is carrying.

If the engine cannot reach minimum RPM. It will lose

horsepower, efficiency, and you may lose the engine. If the engine turns more than the factory rated RPM, your problems are exactly the same. Extreme load differences will require different propellers.

If you can have only one, tailor it to the heaviest load you will encounter and when the vessel is unloaded, use the tachometer.

An example. Try the ski boat. We want to snatch the skier from a deep water start and we need a lower pitch in the propeller in order to do so. Match the propeller to the load and select a pitch that allows full RPM with the skier in tow.

When you do not have the skier in tow, stay off the throttle. You will lose some speed and efficiency, but you will not lose the engine. Two-stroke engines are not designed to lug down and pull big loads at low RPM. They are designed to turn out a lot of horsepower from small displacement and turn a lot of RPM in order to do so.

Special vessels provide special challenges to the propeller shop. An example is the pontoon boat. Trim on the pontoon boat is often dictated by the movement of passengers since they may constitute half the total weight of boat, equipment, and vessel. Move that much weight around in a boat and the vessel must respond accordingly.

The stern of the pontoon boats goes up and down like an elevator. Unless the operator makes a considerable effort to control the distribution of the passengers, propeller selection can be a nightmare. In some extreme cases the only solution may be to bury the propeller and reduce the pitch accordingly

Sailboats are another example of vessels which make extreme demands on the propeller shop. These vessels are going to move at hull speed only and for the sailboat with an outboard auxiliary, this usually means 6 knots or less. Special gear cases and propellers are desirable for this purpose.

Oddly enough, work barges share many common characteristics with the sailboat. They are not so beautiful to behold but they make slow speeds and require special propellers. Amazing things can be done with a properly designed work propeller.

At one time I was using a handmade propeller with 13-3/4 inches of diameter and only six inches of pitch on an ancient 35 horsepower Johnson outboard engine. We used this set up to pull a 40 foot pile driving barge around the marina. The engine could get the job done but only because of that special propeller. That propeller was made for me by the late Louis Bauman of Houston, Texas and it lasted for many years.

We make many tradeoffs in an effort to pull loads with an outboard engine but those we make in the name of speed are even more extreme and certainly more exciting.

Propellers for the bass boat or racing boat are heavily raked, have a lot of lift and a lot of cup. They run high on the transom of the vessel and sacrifice many things to Mercury, the Roman god of speed. These propellers often have a pitch more than twice their diameter. They cavitate heavily before they plane. The boat goes through an exaggerated ugly duckling stage before it finally planes.

When it does plane off, it can fly. The outboard hydroplane is an exaggerated version of the bass boat. Clumsy to a fault in the beginning, it gradually begins to plane. When it first gets up onto the sponsons it still wallows like a pig and at this point it can be scary.

Give it just a second and do not let off the throttle. Here is where the propeller really gets its first solid bite and when the sponsons clear the water, hang on. At 6,000 RPM the propeller had little real hold on the water but from 7,500 RPM all the way to dream land, that propeller is terribly efficient.

Those propellers eventually turn at speeds above 13,000 RPM. The diameter is about 3-3/4 inches and the pitch about 4-1/4 inches. Yet they will load a 100 horsepower engine. Here is another extreme case where gear ratio and adaptation for a special purpose dictate design.

I want you to realize four things.

First, if it is to be satisfactory, the propeller must match the purpose of the vessel.

Second, there are endless numbers or propellers available and the trick to satisfactory selection is more a case of trial and error than any scientific exercise. The propeller expert can probably offer you a good ballpark estimate but you must be ready to invest a bit of time if you hope to get that perfect propeller for your boat.

Third, try before you buy. Most dealers are willing to allow a trial before purchase and so long as you use the propeller only for a test and do it no harm, there is generally no charge.

Fourth, if you are buying a boat because of the advertised performance and you expect a particular speed or other performance from that boat, have the dealer install the propeller and test the boat with that propeller. Not the one that will be delivered in the future. Not the one that is coming someday. The propeller that gives that advertised performance and is on the engine now, before you buy the boat.

I have purposely avoided the matter of specific recommendations for specific purposes. There are simply too many possibilities. Propeller charts are offered by all manufacturers of both factory and after market propellers. Use the chart for a starting place and go from there.

Some manufacturers have a computerized selection chart that contemplates all manner of variables and makes very specific recommendations based upon exact brands and models of boat, even including varieties of load conditions. These charts are wonderful selection tools. They may hit the matched propeller for your purpose on the first try.

Watch how diameter and pitch effect the performance of various vessels as load and use change from day to day. Studious observation will do more to make you a competent propeller person than any other single effort.

CHAPTER TWENTY

SETUP THE ENGINE

Engine setup for the outboard is a problematic and highly controversial subject. It is all too often discussed in terms of absolutes. I want to offer you Fleming's First Law for engine setup: Go easy, go carefully, and go with an open mind. You approach every engine and every vessel as an individual with no preconceptions.

How important is engine set up? The outboard engine must be setup properly to do its job well. The finest engine on earth will not give good service if it is setup incorrectly. On the other hand, the engine must do its part. If your engine is not attaining the proper performance, no amount of set up will make it run well. Always be certain the engine is in a proper state of tune.

When you know the engine itself is operating properly, then you are ready to set the engine up. Before we proceed, let us talk a bit about what setup really is.

Setup is transom height, how high the engine is mounted on the transom. Transom height is effected by the length of the drive shaft housing. Setup considers any setback of the engine which is the distance the engine is mounted aft of the transom. This distance may be affected by the shape of the transom itself. It can also be controlled by the dimensions of a mounting bracket or jacking plate.

Setup is propeller diameter, pitch, and design. When you have selected the engine to match the boat, setup is all those things listed above which are needed to mate the engine to a propeller and a boat. Setup can make or break the marriage between engine and hull.

I want to begin with vessel type. Every vessel is designed for an intended purpose and it has a design speed. The dealer may not tell you this but believe me, it is true. The vessel will do many things, very well, within the limits of the design parameters. Fuel consumption, vessel performance, sea keeping ability and perhaps even the safety of those aboard are hostage to that understanding.

You can use engine setup to compliment those design parameters and the vessel will give all it has to offer. Attempt to do extreme things or ignore common sense and it will punish you for your excesses. No amount of effort expended on setup will enable the vessel to effectively exceed its design parameters.

There is a bit of history which we might consider in order to understand what setup really does. In 1955 a 25 horsepower outboard engine, operated on a runabout or other planing hull, used as much as 50 percent of its power to drive the gear case though the water. This left only 1/2 the power of the engine to actually drive the vessel.

This gear case design was not efficient at higher speeds and it became less efficient as speeds increased. Engine manufacturers knew this amount of drag was excessive but several things had limited the effort to remedy the situation.

First, the public had made no such demand. Speeds on the boats of the day were not too great, and it would cost a great deal to make a basic design change. Also, at that time we did not have propellers available to support innovative mounting systems.

There was little incentive to pursue gear case designs for high engine mountings if there were no propellers which would operate at high mounting elevations. The average boater had never heard of a surface propeller.

In the 1960s engines grew in size, speeds increased and the public became enamored of the fast boat. Manufacturers used speed as a selling point. Gear cases were designed for hydrodynamic considerations, and the race for a perfect propeller was on. Now it was time to tell the public about this new approach to engine set up and why it was important.

The call went out: Raise the engine on the transom. Get that gear case out of the water. The racing fraternity had known for years a gear case would drag much less if there was less of it in the water to drag. They got the first propellers that would operate on the surface. Not surprisingly, the news first came from those professional boat racers.

Get a surface propeller and speeds will go up dramatically. The idea filtered down to the pleasure boat. In the early days this new approach was often misused. Boats which could not benefit from a surface propeller nonetheless got one. There are still an unacceptable number of these seen today.

Raising the engine on the transom of any boat should be approached with caution. Raise it too high and the greater turbulence or water disturbance created by a pleasure boat hull will lead to cavitation and ventilation. It could even cause loss of control. Get it right and the performance increases will be dramatic.

Research in both gear case and propeller design began during the 1960s. We began to hear new terms like rake, lift, and cup added to those old familiar standards such as diameter and pitch. These were the features needed to raise propeller performance to a new level and new developments came in rapid succession.

We discussed the design and performance of propellers in the last chapter. Remember those lessons as we tie together the elements of proper setup which is not separable from a principle element, the propeller.

It is not the intent of this chapter to argue specific amounts of rake, pitch, cup or any other feature of propeller design for a specific applications. I do want you to be aware of those propeller design principles and their effects upon any given hull. I further want you to be able to select your own propellers and set them up properly.

We do have a wide selection of fine propellers to choose from today. The claims and counter claims are legion. It is not easy to chart a course through the difficult channels of this choice.

Let us look at the actual process of engine setup. Our engine is in excellent tune and we are confident of the power source. Begin with transom height and the mounting height of the engine.

How do I decide on a satisfactory mounting? The mounting height of the engine must consider the location of the anti-cavitation plate. This plate controls the movement of water above the propeller and keeps air away from the blades. The relationship between the anti-cavitation plate and the bottom of the vessel is most important. The anti-cavitation plate may be mounted above or below the water, depending upon vessel and propeller design. In making this decision, always consider the use for which the vessel is intended. Mount the engine too high and the propeller will ventilate, too low and the gear case will drag.

A few examples: The offshore, center console will benefit from a fairly high engine mounting. It can give greater speed plus better fuel consumption with a fairly high engine installation. This is a vessel that runs at speed, much of the time, yet it must troll and run the inlets as well.

Mountings with the anti-cavitation plate close to direct alignment with the boat bottom are common and effective. Light to medium cupping for the blades is normal. Your job is to find that last half inch of height that takes the greatest possible amount of gear case out of the water but does not drive the propeller into cavitation or starve the water pump for water.

If the engine is too high, several things will happen. The propeller will cavitate when the vessel jumps off wave tops and this is really hard on engine and gear case. The propeller will cavitate when the vessel is crossing over a wave at low speed and the wave pushes from behind. This can lead to a loss of control at a critical time. The engine may lose cooling water if the mounting is too high. Yet the case will drag, lose performance, and drink fuel if it is too deep. The balance between these diametric opposites is setup.

There are numerous mounting holes in the transom bracket of the engine. Every one of those holes represents a choice and is a large part of this discussion; making those choices. Let us try another example of height selection. This one is at the other extreme from the offshore, center console.

The pontoon boat may require a buried propeller with the anti-cavitation plate well buried. The pontoon boat is designed to carry heavy loads and numerous people, thus the load shifts continuously. A high engine mounting may help the vessel run faster when it is loaded, yet it may be destructive with a full passenger load aboard.

The engine on a pontoon boat must be mounted with consideration of wide variations in vessel trim. This deeper mounting is required because passengers are a mobile cargo that can change the engine height and angle to a drastic degree.

I watched a man start the brand new engine on his pontoon boat and leave it to warm up while the family loaded up. They were all large people and they piled gear on the bow of the boat as they loaded it. Finally they sat on the bow. The engine was running in the air. No water at all. The pontoon boat sat at the dock and the engine ran hotter and hotter until finally it froze tight.

My point is simple. You must match the propeller and the mounting height to the vessel type. You must consider every aspect of vessel operation, what will it do under diverse conditions, and not only top speed. You must consider the engine itself in the equation. How high are the water ports in the gear case? How high will it go and still pump water?

Bass boats have produced great focus on the transom of the boat. Engines on the bass boat often run with the cavitation plate far above the bottom of the boat and one blade of the propeller in the air at all times. In an attempt to get the engine as high as possible, they moved it back from the transom itself on a jacking plate.

The jacking plate is a mechanical device which extends the engine mounting aft of the transom for several inches. Moving the engine back positions the propeller in the harder water and out of the turbulence created by the hull. Now it can be raised even higher. The jacking plate can be raised or lowered as the situation demands.

A manual jacking plate uses a screw device to accomplish this but power assisted models are available. The power assisted jacking plate may be either electric or electric/hydraulic in nature. It is powered by current from the starting battery in the boat. The first jacking plates were used on bass boats but the idea has since received additional converts.

Pleasure boaters looked at the jacking plate and decided to modify the system. They would mount their engines further aft but disregard the elevation change. The result was the modern transom bracket. The transom bracket sets the engine about 30 inches behind the transom.

A great deal of space is saved by doing this and the amount of interior room is increased dramatically. This increase is not accomplished without cost, however. Moving the engine aft adds powerful leverage against the transom, moves the engine's weight, and changes the entire fulcrum (center of balance) of the vessel. Both static and dynamic balance of the vessel are changed. The bow tends to rise precipitately when the seas are on the bow and the stern is deeper in the water. But it does create room in the vessel. Everything is a tradeoff and you must decide what is acceptable as a gain/loss in the trade.

The enormous selection of propellers available may be a curse as well as a blessing. Truth be told, the selection of high-tech propellers available today, probably exceeds our understanding of those lovely creations.

Many vessels enjoy little or no advantage from the use of stainless steel propellers. The propeller is expensive, in many cases it gives no benefit, and it is hard on the gear case.

A runabout designed for 40 miles per hour, or less, will gain little from a stainless steel propeller.

Sailboats, pontoon boats, houseboats, and similar types of vessels are unlikely to benefit from a stainless propeller. The number of vessel types which will not benefit from the stainless steel propeller are legion. The sheer weight of that stainless propeller makes it hard on your gear shift.

Yet, for those instances where they are needed, there is no substitute for a stainless steel propeller. Nothing will run higher or faster than a stainless steel propeller. For the bass boater, river racer, or out and out professional, these props are the only way to go.

Almost any dealer will give you their best advice. The advice of a professional is a useful tool but it cannot supplant practicality. Even the professional will generally admit the best propeller is the one which performs the best. In many cases trial and error is the only route to success.

Knowing this and not wanting to be faced with a dissatisfied customer, virtually any boat dealer or marina owner will lend you a propeller for a day if you bought the boat from them. Almost any propeller manufacturer will lend a propeller if they believe the loan may lead to a sale.

High speed photography, computer modeling, and modern techniques have told us a great deal about propeller design, but oddly enough, there is still a great deal propeller men still do not agree upon. The vast diversity of designs practically guarantees that here is no consensus opinion or universal knowledge.

The late Allen Smith of Shreveport Louisiana, built propellers that held many speed records, both A. P. B. A. and N. O. A. His advice was sought by numerous members of the racing fraternity in the '50s, '60s, and later. He told me, "Boy, propellers are a voodoo science. Nobody really understands propellers." This from a man who was a wizard in his field.

Set aside the necessary time to set up your boat and you will be glad you did. When you have discovered the perfect propeller and the very best setup for your boat, be sure to protect it with a record of the details. Your ship's log is a good place to keep track of your present setup and any details of propeller design, repitch, or special conditions.

CHAPTER TWENTY-ONE

A MEASURE OF EFFICIENCY & PERFORMANCE

Advertising is a game. The Madison Avenue native has elevated the business of advertising to a fine art in which many impressions can be conveyed with very little substance. Results seldom match expectations. Small wonder in an age where we expend lavish superlatives on a can of cat food.

The matters of efficiency and performance are seldom what they are suggested to be. he capabilities of an engine may not always match the advertisements provided to the prospective buyer.

Before we get too far into this discussion, let us decide how we are going to compare engines, propellers, boats, etc. I will begin with the engine. Engines should only be compared by dynamometer test. The test should last for one hour, minimum. From the dynamometer we will learn exactly how much horsepower the engine develops and at what RPM. We will see how much torque the engine develops and at what RPM.

By maintaining a fuel flow chart we will know how many gallons of fuel per hour the engine burns, at any given increment. Now we can say with certainty how many gallons/pounds of fuel the engine burns for each horsepower/hour. At this point we have a fair set of figures on which to compare any two engines.

There are other measures of engine efficiency. Each of these descriptions will be accompanied by a mathematical calculation and those calculations will be complete, with one exception, which will become apparent as you read further.

One of the best comparisons of engine performance is a fuel consumption figure expressed in gallons per horsepower/hour. This is the amount of fuel, measured in gallons, which is required for a given engine to develop one horsepower for a period of one hour. We are going to calculate that figure for a sample engine.

The engineer makes the fuel calculations in terms of pounds of fuel rather than gallons. For the sake of simplicity, I will make the necessary calculations to change pounds of fuel to gallons of fuel and we will use that measurement.

Gallons per horsepower/hour is a figure easily calculated from dynamometer measurements. It is both an accurate figure and a meaningful figure, but it is never published.

Begin with the engine attached to a dynamometer and running properly. The engine is developing 55 horsepower at this time and the fuel flow meter shows a consumption of 5.5 gallons per hour.

Divide 55 horsepower into 5.5 gallons of fuel consumed in one hour and we find we are using 0.1 gallons of fuel per horsepower/hour.

This is about a normal figure for a 55 horsepower, two-stroke engine at full throttle. The gallons (or pounds) per horsepower/hour figure is also the only fair way to compare two engines, if fuel efficiency is the question. This comparison cannot be made on a boat.

The problem with trying to make similar comparisons on a boat, derive from the fact you cannot say with any precision, how much horsepower or torque it is developing at a given time. You are comparing one rig to another and the boat, load, propeller, and setup are a part of that performance.

On a dynamometer you can calculate fuel consumption in gallons per horsepower/hour for any engine at any speed. You can find the most economical speed for the engine you own or see how it stacks up against other engines. The dynamometer is an impartial judge and gives a fair, honest decision, every time

Engines of every size and brand should be subjected to this test and the figures published. The reason this figure is ignored by advertisers becomes clear when we begin to see there is not a lot of difference between engines, when measured by this device.

There is one other measurement of engine performance. This measurement is called Thermal Efficiency and the thermal efficiency of any engine you wish to test will be universally horrible. This is true from engine to engine and brand to brand.

Thermal efficiency is a measurement of horsepower/ hours developed by an engine, from a given quantity of fuel consumed, expressed as a fraction of the potential horsepower/hours of energy contained in that amount of fuel. To make this calculation we will need to know two things:

The first are:

1. How many gallons of fuel did our test engine consume during the one hour test?

2. How many horsepower/hours did it produce while consuming that amount of fuel.

That will give the first figure which we need to know. What did we actually accomplish?

The second figures we require are:

3. How many BTU's of heat energy are actually available from the fuel that we consumed.

4. How many potential horsepower/hours does it represent?

This will produce the second figure we need. The

potential amount of horsepower/hours which might have resulted from our test, if the engine were 100 percent efficient.

Here is a table of measurements used in our calculations:

One horsepower/hour equals 2,544 BTU's of heat energy (approximately).

There are 21,400 BTU's of heat energy in a pound of gasoline (approximately).

There are 125,600 BTU's of heat energy in a gallon of gasoline (approximately).

Gasoline for instance is given at 125,400 BTU's of heat energy by one source and at 125, 800 BTU's by another source. My conversion chart is based upon the average of the two. The calculation in the above example may be a few BTU's off, because of a specific fuel, but the results are truly representative of those which you can expect from a modern engine.

As in the previous paragraphs, I have made the calculations needed to change pounds of fuel to gallons and, as before, our calculations will be made in terms of gallons per horsepower/hour.

Let us consider the V-6 engine of our present day which usually develops about 225 horsepower from 22.5 gallons of gasoline, per hour, at full throttle. Multiply 225 horsepower by a single hour and we find our test engine produced 225 horsepower/hours from those 22.5 gallons of fuel.

This is what we have actually accomplished. Now we need to know what was the potential, in horsepower/hours, available from the fuel we burned.

We can see in the conversion chart there are 125,600 BTU's of heat energy in a gallon of average gasoline. Our test engine burned 22.5 of those gallons during the one hour test. Those 22.5 gallons had a value of 2,826,000 BTU's of heat energy (125,600 x 22.5). These are the potential BTU's of heat energy in the fuel we consumed.

What is the horsepower potential? Our conversion chart also tells us that there are 2,544 British Thermal Units (BTU's) of heat energy in one horsepower. We could produce 1110.85 horsepower from that amount of fuel, at 100 percent efficiency (2,826,000 divided by 2,544).

Our potential is 1110.85 horsepower/hours from 22.5 gallons of fuel. Divide 225 horsepower/hours, which we achieved, by those 1110.85 horsepower hours we should have achieved and we find that the engine has a thermal efficiency of 0.2025. It is just a bit over 20 percent efficient.

We are wasting almost 80 percent of every gallon of fuel we run through this engine. This is not an indictment of the outboard engine manufacturers as an industry, but rather of our society as a whole. The outboard engine manufacturers build an excellent engine, within the limits posed by our present designs.

The piston engine is simply not a very efficient way to make power. We actually know this and we, as a society, have not demanded better. Thus, the internal combustion engine is all we have.

If you compare all engines on the basis of thermal efficiency, essentially every engine make and model comes very close to this norm. Some are slightly over 20 percent and a few are slightly under.

There is another useful measurement which does seem to help grade engines on the basis of design, Volumetric Efficiency. When the piston goes down on the intake stroke, a fresh charge of air or air/fuel mix will be drawn into the cylinder. The pressure of that charge will always be less than atmospheric.

Restrictions in the intake system such as venturis (constrictions), flow friction, (air does drag on the walls of any conduit), reed valve loss, and loss from direction changes, each takes its toll. Butterflies for choke and throttle add to this mix.

Atmospheric pressure is the maximum potential that a naturally aspirated engine can attain. The pressure on the new charge when it partially fills the cylinder is the best result the engine actually can attain. The comparison is called volumetric efficiency.

An example? Assume that your engine has a charge of 12.9 lbs/in^2 in the cylinder, as it rotates.

The potential is 14.7 lbs/in^2 in the atmosphere and we have 12.9 lbs/in^2 in the cylinder. Use the formula below:

$$12.9 \text{ lbs./in}^2 \,/\, 14.7 \text{ lbs/in}^2 = 0.878 \text{ (percent efficient)}$$

The volumetric efficiency of your own engine would not be so easy to calculate since we do not have the first figure, initial cylinder pressure. This too can be calculated but the process requires either an advanced piece of software or high mathematics.

I will not run through that ordeal but I will tell you this; volumetric efficiency speaks volumes for the engines ability to make horsepower, efficiently. It controls the amount of air/fuel mix going into the cylinder and consequently it is the major factor in how much horsepower we can get from a given number of cubic inches.

The next form of efficiency is propeller efficiency. First, let us consider the pitch of the propeller. Our propeller has a pitch of 24 inches, a gear ratio in the lower unit of 2.0:1 and the engine is turning at 5500 RPM

Convert the propeller pitch to feet. We see:

$$24 \text{ inches pitch} \,/\, 12 \text{ inches} = 2 \text{ feet of pitch}$$

Divide the 2.0 gear ratio into the number of engine revolutions. 2.0 divided into 5500 RPM is a speed of 2750 RPM at the propeller. If the vessel has a potential of 2 feet of travel for every engine RPM, multiply 2 feet by 2750 engine RPM and the is speed of 5,500 feet per minute. Again, this is a potential.

Convert the feet per minute to miles per minute. There are 5,280 feet in each mile. Divide 5,500 feet per minute by

5,280 feet per mile which equals 1.042 miles per minute. 1.042 miles per minute, multiplied by 60 minutes, yields a potential speed of 62.52 miles per hour.

If this propeller was one hundred percent efficient that would be the speed over the water. With a radar gun or a good GPS, check the actual speed and compare it to the potential speed. The difference is the amount of slip or loss from the propeller.

The mathematical comparison is stated as propeller efficiency. High speed hulls, those that reach speeds of 70 miles per hour or more, should have a propeller efficiency close to 90 percent. Those which operate at lower speeds, 35 miles per hour to 55 miles per hour, should have a propeller efficiency around 85 percent.

Vessels that are slow moving and heavily loaded should drop into the 80 percent efficiency range. If the number is below that figure, you might want to look at your propeller selection again. A last look at propeller efficiency is one that we will consider on a practical basis rather than a mathematical basis.

Propellers with large diameters and less pitch, the load or work propeller, are more efficient in reverse. The design of the wheel is not loaded for top end performance to the same degree as those propellers designed for very high speed. If control is a problem for your vessel, consider the style of propeller you select on that basis.

There are cheap calculators designed to make only those mathematical calculations concerned with propeller efficiency. They are available from most of the better ships chandlers and marinas around the country. They do most of this work for you and save a great deal of time.

I have gone though the entire process so you may see where the figures come from. It is important to understand the underpinnings as well as the finished structure.

How about hull efficiency and a basis for the comparison of complete rigs? I like to measure the engine separately on the dynamometer so I will know what I had to start with, now how do I find what the whole rig is doing? One of the measurements I like is the ton/mile. This measurement begins with the weight of your vessel, expressed in tons.

If the vessel weighs 2200 pounds it also weighs 2.1 ton (divide the actual weight by 2,000 pounds in a ton). Move that vessel one mile and you have 2.1 ton/miles. Conversely, if the vessel weighs less than 2,000 pounds you have only a fraction of a ton. For a 1600 pound vessel you get 0.80 tons.

This vessel would rate 0.80 ton/miles for each mile traveled. What do we do with this figure? Divide the ton/miles of weight moved into the gallons of fuel consumed in its movement and you have an excellent measurement of the performance of engine/vessel/propeller.

An example. Suppose we use that first vessel with a 2.1 ton/mile rating. We run the engine for one hour and the vessel covers 12 miles. Multiply 12 miles by the 2.1 rating and we get 25.2 ton/miles. Assume that the engine burns 5.7 gallons of gasoline over that distance. Now divide 25.2 ton/miles into 5.7 gallons of fuel and we see that our engine burns 0.226 gallons per ton/mile.

We now have a perfectly fair basis on which to compare two different rigs. Be certain the speeds are the same for both vessels when the comparison is made. Of course, you can use this equation as an instrument to compare the performance of your own vessel at various speeds and various loads.

You will be surprised at how much the ton/mile calculation reveals about the vessel you are running. If you feel less than enthused with the numbers you get at one particular speed, at all speeds, at one particular loading or at all loading, consider the propeller selection before you become too disappointed. You already know how to calculate propeller efficiency. Use that knowledge.

Perhaps the oldest calculation and the first one we learn to make is miles per gallon. This is an easy one. Take the speed of the boat in miles per hour from a GPS (Global Positioning System). Take the fuel consumption in gallons per hour from a flow meter. Then divide gallons per hour into miles per hour. The result is miles per gallon.

An example. Your flow meter shows 12 gallons per hour, the GPS shows 24 miles per hour. Divide 12 into 24 and we get 2 miles per gallon. This is also a good indicator of efficiency but it is again a measure of the engine, prop and vessel efficiency as a combination. Use it but also understand it. In using this figure, you are comparing rigs as a whole, not engines alone.

Remember these things:

The two-stroke engine is a wonderful creation. Like all internal combustion engines, it is very inefficient. Again, like all those other engines, it wastes at least 75 percent of the fuel it burns. But for the present, it is all we have.

There are many ways to compare engines and many other ways to compare rigs as a whole. If you will use the calculations shown in this chapter, always remembering which ones apply to the engine alone and which ones apply to the whole rig, you will be well on the way to the truth.

CHAPTER TWENTY-TWO

TROUBLESHOOTING

For many years the troubleshooting of an outboard engine was a comparatively simple task. Did the engine have even compression? If it did not, the engine had to be systematically disassembled and inspected in stages until the problem became apparent. This situation has not changed.

With the older engines, if the engine had even and sufficient compression, the problems that plagued the two-stroke likely to be ignition. Probably 65 percent to 70 percent of the engine problems on an engine equipped with a make and break ignition system derived from that system.

Points, condensers, plug wires, and spark plugs themselves were easily inspected and the necessary corrections were generally apparent to the mechanic. As engines became more sophisticated, problems for the technician became more complex.

There were no longer any points to be inspected. Troubleshooting became the province of various kinds of testers, those little black boxes. The old time mechanics often eschewed these testers in favor of special intuition or a sensitive ear which all of us who have lived a few extra years are purported to possess. Education was lagging behind technology and there was another factor at work also.

Many mechanics of yesteryear were wont to say, "I took this job to get away from all those books in the first place. I'm not about to start no math class just to learn how to do somethin' I been workin' at for fifteen years." This rejection was more widespread than one would think and the public suffered for it.

In all fairness, their intuition did offer a number of answers and many times they were the right answers. That sensitive ear could hear many things. Surges in speed were generally fuel related while stuttering or skipping sounds were generally spark deficiencies, though this was not an entirely reliable assumption.

Today, the technician is favored with an engine which can be largely diagnosed by a lap top computer. Plug it in, read the dials and replace the appropriate parts. The home mechanic, the enterprising do-it-yourselfer, is out on his ear. The seat-of-the-pants mechanic is also outdated.

If you would like to make repairs to an outboard engine, first get a proper service manual. All of the information you need is contained in those pages. Next, remember the lessons you have learned in this book. Revere that service manual like a mechanic's bible but do not put your brain to sleep.

The service manual will tell you how to do things to make the engine run; the knowledge which you have gained here, will help you understand why the steps you are about to take are necessary. It will also help you understand why those steps will accomplish the purpose which you intend.

What if the recommended processes in that service manual do not entirely satisfy? Then the knowledge which you have gained here will help you to understand why. The man who knows how to do a job on the engine will always have a job, but the man who knows why, will always be his boss.

Remember, not everything is mechanical or electronic. Many things are still mental and there is much that requires thought.

Let me tell you some of those things that remain: The old time compression check is still a very reliable diagnostic tool. If there is a compression loss as great as 15 lbs/in^2 from minimum factory specifications, the engine has a mechanical problem. If there is as much as 15 lbs/in^2 variation in compression from the highest to the lowest cylinder, the engine has a problem and nothing the lap top can offer will save a tear down.

Figure 23

Small errors can create large problems as it did for this badly burnt piston.

Modern two-stroke engines run on the edge. Compression pressures, cylinder temperatures, ignition timing and fuel/air ratios are all running right at border line. Very small errors in the computer, and the engine is gone. The compression check is still a most important diagnostic tool.

Not every engine is electronic and there are many problems that we still seek by other means. Diagnosis should be pursued in a logical manner. Make no conclusions until you have checked the engine out thoroughly and gathered as much information about the engine as you can. Then proceed.

Figure 24

The matching cylinder head to the above piston.

Remember everything you have learned on these pages. The engine requires Air, Fuel, and Spark. All in the proper proportions. At the proper time. It must have even and sufficient compression. If it has all of these things it will run properly. If it does not run properly, the problem lies in one of those categories listed above.

Fuel and electrical problems are to be pursued backwards. Begin at the end and work back. If you suspect the engine has an ignition problem, begin at the spark plug and work your way backwards to the battery. Check every electrical component, in order.

If you believe the engine has a fuel problem, begin at the carburetor or injector. If there is no fuel or not enough pressure here, start working back, all the way to the fuel tank. You were not trying to run on empty, were you?

Water or temperature problems are no different. Start with the telltale hole. If you do not see water at this point, work your way back, through the thermostat hoses, right down to the water pump. If the engine has run hot, for whatever reason, always run a compression check. The new engines do not like to overheat, ever.

You may want to inspect the engine you plan to buy a bit more closely today. That inspection may tell you a bit about how difficult the engine will be for you or any mechanic to repair.

The pan, cowl and drive shaft housing are the most commonly seen portions of the engine. The power head is the most common area of repair or maintenance and much of it is hidden away beneath the cowling. Sadly, the most lasting impression of the engine is the one made by the external parts. The paint and the logo, the bright and the fancy, are the things which the prospective buyer notices on the showroom floor. Unlike the buyers of automobiles, few boaters ever raise the hood and look before they leap.

It may be worthwhile to remove the cowling from any engine that you intend to buy and see how accessible the parts are. There are outboard engines on the showroom floors that are a nightmare to service. That will effect the cost of repairs to your engine.

I looked at a V-6 outboard engine recently that required the removal of all six of the ignition coils and part of the wiring harness, simply to replace a spark plug. The instances that require removal of parts to access the one you were trying to service were going to be fairly common.

One of the phenomena that must be recognized in dealing with electronic engines is the matter of spurious emissions. These emissions may be the use of the wrong spark plug. The plug can actually emit RF signals which can trigger the ECM. High voltage transmission lines, two-way radios, fish finders, and endless numbers of other devices may create electronic waves that will disturb the engines computer. Great strides have been made in the suppression of these waves and shielding of the computer. Yet we still have many instances when stray emissions attack your ECMs. Except for mechanical breakdown, this is the only problem the lap top does not diagnose. A perfectly reasonable assumption is, if you have run all the tests on the lap top and the engine still gives you trouble, there are two possibilities. Either the problem is mechanical or it is something the lap top is not programmed to diagnose. Spurious emissions are about the only thing that fits the mold. Even worse, those spurious emissions may be intermittent.

If you enter and leave the area where those emissions derive, the lap top will show nothing for the technician to find. The engine will operate properly when tested. Neither electronic diagnosis nor old time intuition will solve the problem.

If you are a mechanic or a do-it-yourselfer, you must not use this as an excuse and lump every knotty problem into the category of spurious emissions. This must not become a catchall excuse for a technician who has not done the job. At the same time, it is important to know those types of problems do exist.

If you cannot fix that engine yourself, why are we talking about troubleshooting? If you truly assimilate the information found on these pages you will know how the engine works and you will know why the engine works. You will be better able to give your mechanic an insight into what is causing your engine to give less than satisfactory performance. That insight can save time and money.

What will our future outboard engine look like? Some of the electronic spikes that trouble our engines may be caused by the accessories such as the alternator. Some of those spurious emissions may also be created by accessories on the engine. In an effort to control all phases of engine operation we are going to see a new generation of engines that are totally electronic.

The temperature, oil pressure, fuel supply, charge voltage, and indeed every facet of engine operation will be controlled by the ECM. A bit much? It is not three years away. The engine will change so fast in the next generation, you will not recognize it ten years from now.

Many of those changes will be for the better, and a few will miss the mark. It is the new millennium and as the Chinese said, "The only thing that is constant is change itself."

CHAPTER TWENTY-THREE

A BIT OF HISTORY

The history of a fabulous and storied industry in a few short paragraphs. This is so presumptuous as to be foolish but I will even compound the madness by writing this chapter from memory. The result may not qualify as research but it is the recollections of a man who lived and breathed much of that history. From 1930 until the present day, I was there. I saw it all happen.

There is a great deal of controversy over who invented the first outboard engine. In an effort to settle the matter, historians generally adopted a new term. Instead of the first outboard engine we now speak of the first successful outboard engine. Credit for this engine is generally given to Ole Evinrude.

I will separate this history into two chronological parts and separate engines into those same two areas. Engines built after 1903 and before 1949 I will refer to as "early" engines. Those built after 1949 we shall call "late style" engines. I picked 1949 as a breaking point because of three things.

First, it marked the beginning of predominantly aluminum engines to replace those made of cast iron. Second, it was the start of the serious manufacture of alternate firing, twin cylinder engines. Third, this year was to produce the first auxiliary fuel tank and the first real forward-neutral-reverse gear shift.

Each of these was a very important innovation. To have

171

so many exciting and important features added to our engines in a single year is a stunning accomplishment. Those improvements have all lasted until this day and so, I recognize 1949 as a pivotal year in the development of the two-stroke outboard engine.

1903
OLE EVINRUDE BUILDS THE FIRST SUCCESSFUL OUTBOARD ENGINE

I begin with 1903 because it was the year of Ole Evinrude's first successful outboard engine. There is a great deal of controversy about who actually built the first outboard engine. History now uses the term "successful" to describe Evinrude's engine and he is considered to have developed the first of these.

1903 TO 1930
THE DOMINANT YEARS

I think of this as the Cast Iron Era. The cylinder block and most of the remainder of the engine, built during those years were made of cast iron. The crankcase and mounting bracket were generally the only aluminum castings on the engine. They were ungainly.

These engines were characterized by heavy weight, opposed pistons, long connecting rods, internal rotary valves, and slow speeds (about 4,000 RPM). The fuel tanks were mounted on the engine. Of course, that big square fuel tank did nothing for the aesthetics of the engine and it required a messy refuel about every 45 minutes to one hour of operation.

During those early years, Evinrude and Johnson engines were the dominant brands. There were other manufacturers building outboard engines, companies with names like Caille Red Head and Muncie, which have since faded into oblivion.

1930 TO 1939
THE YEARS OF AWAKENING

I call these the Years of Awakening because this was a time when the nation began to embrace the outboard engine and the boating style it would foster. The growing popularity of the outboard engine prompted others to enter the market. There were some rather innovative engines which showed up during this period.

One of these was the Clark Troller. This was a 7/8ths horsepower engine that ran underwater. The engine was enclosed in a module which resembled the gear case on a modern outboard and ran below the surface of the water.

During these early years the Evinrude and Johnson engines dominated outboard racing. The custom modified engines of men like Carl Hubbel were dominant on the racing circuits of this country. Pop Jacoby built the early hydroplanes for the Hubbel creations and Evinrude/Jacoby was a common sight in the winners circle and on the APBA record books.

These were Golden Years for the Evinrude /Johnson engines but serious competition was just over the horizon. The year 1939 was to see the beginning of a real change in the way outboard engines were designed and built. War clouds were gathering and government contracts would effect the industry.

1939 To 1945
THE COMING OF KIEKHAEFER & THE
ALTERNATE FIRING TWIN

The coming of World War II brought innovation and change to the outboard industry. The need for light, high-speed, engines for small landing craft, caused the government to buy outboard engines at a frantic pace. The manufacturers of these engines were also commissioned to provide power heads for auxiliary fire pumps, generators, etc.

In the early Forties we began to see the mention of alternate firing twins in advertising literature and to see these engines on boats across America. These engines had the pistons/cylinders in line above each other. The older opposed piston engine fired both cylinders at the same time with only one power impulse per revolution.

These were still cast iron engines but they could also be thought of as transition engines. The alternate firing twin divided the power impulses evenly between the cylinders at 180 degrees apart. It was lighter, slimmer, and ran more smoothly. This was a move in the right direction for the two-stroke engine and it would be the harbinger of things to come. It set the stage for what was to be the Modern Era

Lou Fageol turned a Crosley automobile engine on end and mounted it atop an outboard lower unit. This was the first successful four-stroke outboard and it was Made In America. It would never challenge Evinrude/Johnson for supremacy but it did find a niche in the market. Lou Fageol lost interest in the project an sold the patents to Homelite.

Homelite marketed the engine for several years under the name, Bear Cat and finally sold it to Fisher-Pierce. Fisher-Pierce marketed the engine in conjunction with their very popular Boston Whaler boats and the engine survived until the 1950s.

About this time a man named Carl Kiekhaefer began to do very exciting things. He made a few false starts but then he hit the jackpot.

In the early Forties, Mr. Kiekhaefer began to build a pair of outboard engines under the name, Mercury. There was a single cylinder, 3 horsepower engine and a twin cylinder, 6 horsepower engine. The twin was an in-line, alternate firing engine but it had ball and roller bearings throughout.

At first glance, this was just another pair of small engines. Their significance was lost on many boaters and the industry as a whole. Yet from these humble beginnings came an engine that could turn very high revolutions and was just a bit stronger than most engines with similar horsepower ratings.

Along with the Evinrude and Johnson factories, the Kiekhaefer Tool & Die Works turned to War Production and the dark clouds over Europe managed to obscure the pleasure boating world for several years. But we learned a lot during World War II.

1945 To 1949
THE WAR ENDS

In these years our country changed from a wartime economy to a peacetime economy. Spendable income was in short supply as factory after factory closed its door or scaled back on production. America was looking for a new direction. Not a great deal was happening in the world of outboard engines.

1949
THE INDUSTRY CHANGES
THE COMPETITION BEGINS

In 1949 we would see several new innovations from the Evinrude camp. They introduced an alternate firing, aluminum blocked, engine called *Fast Twin.* This engine had the first auxiliary fuel tank on an outboard engine. It had a two line fuel system which used crankcase compression from the engine to pressurize the fuel tank and force fuel back up to the engine.

This engine also had a gear shift with a full Forward-Neutral-Reverse. The gear shift was a handy addition and it brought a lot of business to the manufacturer. This was the first engine with a full cowling and it had good appearance. Those years were an exciting time for the industry and it was about ready to explode.

In the same year, 1949, Mercury Marine gave us the twin cylinder, alternate firing, Mercury Lightning engines. They had a full jeweled powerhead, as the advertising claimed. Ball and roller bearings graced every moving part in the engine. It also brought attention to the caged reed valve system, which was another Kiekhaefer invention.

The horsepower was grossly underrated. The engine displaced 18.98 cubic inches and it was rated 10 horsepower at 4,000 RPM. What the advertising failed to state was this: The engine would rev freely to 5,500 RPM and develop almost twice the rated horsepower. Moreover, it would turn at those speeds and live.

I took those engines out of the box and won races with them. This engine, more than any other, was to start the quest for light, high speed power to drive a pleasure boat...fast! That first Mercury Lightning also had a full cowling and a streamlined appearance but it lacked the refinements of the Evinrude Fast Twin.

1950 TO 1959
THE YEARS OF GROWTH

In 1950 Mr. Kiekhaefer delivered his Hurricane. This engine was still rated at 10 horsepower. It displaced 20 cubic inches, had four more reeds in the valve cage, and it was a bomb. On an outboard hydroplane the Hurricane 10 was the hottest thing since soap. The horsepower rating was a joke, and by this time, everybody knew it.

On a fishing boat it gave speeds to equal much larger engines and it was still light enough to carry. The Mercury Marine logo was becoming synonymous with speed and it has not lost that image. The engine still had the tank on the motor and it still lacked a gear shift, but it would fly.

Mercury Marine was pushing the envelope, fueling the drive for faster and lighter engines. Evinrude and Johnson were pushing convenience and adaptation. There was no looking back and both companies had to be aware of what the competition was about.

By the coming of the 1954 models, Evinrude/Johnson

would expand the use of auxiliary fuel tanks to all their engines of 5 horsepower and above. Mercury Marine had adopted this system on its full line, 20 horsepower and above. The separate tank was a very popular innovation. Both companies had built still larger and faster engines to top out the lines and the race was on.

In 1954, Mercury Marine introduced the Mark 20-H. This engine had a 20 cubic inch power head and a small streamlined gear case which was dubbed Quicksilver. That engine is still competitive as an APBA, B-Stock outboard racing engine.

In the late 50s our outboard engines progressed rapidly through the horsepower ranges. As they did, we needed larger cylinder displacements and different cylinder configurations to achieve those horsepower increases. Engines with a V-4 cylinder configuration came from the Evinrude/Johnson factories in 1956 while in-line, 6 cylinder engines emerged from Mercury's facilities.

1959 TO 1969
ENTER THE LOOPER

The first three cylinder Tripple outboard engine, made in this country, was a product of the Evinrude/Johnson company. It was also the first real loop-charged outboard engine. This engine was introduced in 1959 as a 55 horsepower unit and it is still in use today.

It has gone through a number of refinements and had the displacement upped a bit, but that was a rock solid piece of engineering that has stood the test of time. With a 70 horsepower rating, it is still sold in largely the same shape as it appeared in 1959. A fine design that is yet worth a second look to anyone interested in engines of that size.

Probably 80 percent of the two-stroke engines in use today employ that loop charged design and the loop-charged engine becomes a more dominant design every year.

This also had one of the earliest Capacitive Discharge Ignition systems. The pointless ignition was a real breakthrough since it ended the need to replace points and condensers at frequent intervals. It also provided a hotter spark on a more reliable basis.

1969 TO 1979

During this period, outboard engines from foreign manufacturers, began to make inroads into the American market. Suzuki Marine and Yamaha Marine began a slow but inexorable march towards recognition as a power in the outboard market. These engines brought with them a number of innovations that were embraced by U. S. boaters.

The first Automatic Oiling Systems appeared on these engines and the reason was easily understood. Both companies had been manufacturing two-stroke motorcycles for many years and both companies employed a remote oil supply with a metering device or pump to mix the oil with the gasoline.

A new and serious pair of players had joined the game. They were new kids on the block but they were determined competitors. Their influence on the outboard engine market would be quickly felt.

1979 TO 1989
THE YEARS OF THE Vs

The V-6 engine made its debut in 1979. It was an instant success. The horsepower race was on again. The first American-made automatic oiling systems appeared on the V-6 engines. Available horsepower climbed over 150. It would finally hit 225 horsepower and continue to soar.

1989 TO PRESENT
THE ELECTRONIC YEARS

In 1989 the Suzuki Marine Corporation introduced its first Electronic Fuel Injector (EFI) on a 150 horsepower outboard engine. Mercury Marine Corporation also entered the EFI race with its XR-2 Bass boat special. Suzuki Marine would rapidly expand its application of the EFI principle to most of its higher horsepower models and Mercury Marine did the same.

The OMC Corporation (Evinrude/Johnson) never marketed an EFI system. They were ready with the *Ficht* Direct Fuel Injector when the industry became emissions conscious. Mercury Marine introduced a DFI unit called Opti-Max which filled the low emissions bill. The Electronic Control Module came into existence in this period.

The ECM would coordinate spark and fuel injector functions. This was the beginning of an engine that could be totally controlled with all facets of its operation running on a tight leash. The electronic age had come to the outboard engine. Sound, fuel consumption, and exhaust smoke were greatly reduced.

Much of the credit for those electronic wonder works should be given to the Federal Government. Emissions limits were set for outboard engines by the Environmental Protection Agency and the engine manufacturers were left with little choice.

THE YEAR 2000

Mercury Marine introduced the first fully electronic, multi-point, oil injection system. This unit injects carefully measured amounts of lubricant to those areas where it is needed most.

ACROSS THE YEARS

A few interesting engines have fallen through the cracks. In the late '50s and early '60s the Evinrude/Johnson camp licensed a number of engines which were built from the same parts as their own brand-name engines. These engines had names such as Gale Products, *Buccaneer*, Spiegel, *Brooklure*, Goodyear, *Sea Bee*, Atlas, *Royal*, and Montgomery Ward, *Sea King*. There were several others whose names are less well known.

Mercury Marine once marketed a clone named *Wizard* through the Western Auto Super Stores. The West Bend Aluminum Company, manufacturers of pressure cookers, also created an outboard engine which bore their name. It was eventually sold to the Chrysler Corporation and the engine was renamed, *Chrysler/West Bend.* Later it was renamed *Force* and the entire manufacturing responsibility fell upon the shoulders of Mercury Marine. That engine alone, of all those small brands listed, was to survive and be revered by the industry and the boater alike. In 1999 Mercury Marine manufactured the last Force engine.

The cauldron of time has now boiled the many engine builders down to a few. There were many other outboard engine makers in days of yore but this is not a complete history. In fact, it is only a smattering, but I hope you have found it entertaining.

2000 AND BEYOND
WHAT NEXT?

Just a glimpse or two. How about fully electronic engines with controls for temperature, alternator output, fuel and ignition? Shucks, that is not a real prediction, those engines are already on the drawing board.

How about alternate fuels? Maybe Hi-Fuel? Hi- Fuel is liquid hydrogen. Burn it and the by product is plain water. No hydrocarbons, no carbon in the engine. This stuff burns very clean and it is the logical successor to petroleum based fuels.

A really different engine design? How about a constant speed, gas turbine that pulls an electric generator for power. Less weight than our present engines and as much as 35 percent more efficient. That gas turbine has potential that really excites an engine lover.

I will leave you with a final thought. I have enjoyed writing this book. I hope you have enjoyed reading it. If you did, there are others in the series covering the four-stroke, marine gas engine (*Complete Guide to Gasoline Marine Engines*) and the diesel engine (*Complete Guide to Diesel Engines*). I'm sure you will want to pick up a copy of each!

Books published by
Bristol Fashion Publications
Free catalog, phone 1-800-478-7147

Boat Repair Made Easy — Haul Out
Written By John P. Kaufman

Boat Repair Made Easy — Finishes
Written By John P. Kaufman

Boat Repair Made Easy — Systems
Written By John P. Kaufman

Boat Repair Made Easy — Engines
Written By John P. Kaufman

Standard Ship's Log
Designed By John P. Kaufman

Large Ship's Log
Designed By John P. Kaufman

Designing Power & Sail
Written By Arthur Edmunds

Building A Fiberglass Boat
Written By Arthur Edmunds

Buying A Great Boat
Written By Arthur Edmunds

Boater's Book of Nautical Terms
Written By David S. Yetman

Practical Seamanship
Written By David S. Yetman

Captain Jack's Basic Navigation
Written By Jack I. Davis

Creating Comfort Afloat
Written By Janet Groene

Living Aboard
Written By Janet Groene

Racing The Ice To Cape Horn
Written By Frank Guernsey & Cy Zoerner

Marine Weather Forecasting
Written By J. Frank Brumbaugh

Complete Guide To Gasoline Marine Engines
Written By John Fleming

Complete Guide To Outboard Engines
Written By John Fleming

Complete Guide To Diesel Marine Engines
Written By John Fleming

Trouble Shooting Gasoline Marine Engines
Written By John Fleming

Trailer Boats
Written By Alex Zidock

Skipper's Handbook
Written By Robert S. Grossman

White Squall
The Last Voyage Of Albatross
Written By Richard E. Langford

Cruising South
What to Expect Along The ICW
Written By Joan Healy

Electronics Aboard
Written By Stephen Fishman

Five Against The Sea
A True Story of Courage & Survival
Written By Ron Arias

Scuttlebutt
Seafaring History & Lore
Written By Captain John Guest USCG Ret.

Cruising The South Pacific
Written By Douglas Austin

Catch of The Day
How To Catch, Clean & Cook It
Written By Carla Johnson

VHF Marine Radio Handbook
Written By Mike Whitehead

REVIEWS

Southern Boating - Jerry Renninger

Somewhere in this solar system there's probably an individual who knows as much about marine engines as John Fleming, but if so, it's doubtful that he writes with equal clarity on this highly technical and complex subject.

Mark Klossner - Mercury Marine
Dealer Training Manager, Mercury University

"Bravo to John Fleming for translating the technical jargon of marine propulsion in a way that's easy for everyone to understand. His three books, *Complete Guide To Outboard Engines, Complete Guide To Gasoline Marine Engines,* and *Complete Guide To Diesel Marine Engines* are well-written, thoughtfully laid out and very informative. They should be required reading for anyone who owns, fixes or sells marine engines!"

ABOUT THE AUTHOR

John Fleming

John Fleming has conducted a 60 year love affair with engines and never met one he did not like. There have been a few that were so exciting he remembers them like an old flame but they all serve a purpose and they are all a part of my memories.

The first engine he built was a 1948 model, 4.2 horsepower, Champion outboard engine. He was 9 years old which made it monumental task. To see and hold the parts his father had described was fascinating.

He held a United States Coast Guard, 500 ton masters ticket and has a total of more than 3,000 days at sea.

John has run boats of many types and varieties in 44 States and 3 countries: crossed the Okefenokee in an airboat and canoe, ran the Everglades from Flamingo Park to Chokloskee Island and from Whitewater Bay to the head of the Little Shark River.

For eight years he held a State of Florida Teachers Certificate to teach engine repair in the State.

John and his wife have run delivery charters across the Gulf of Mexico from Brownsville, Texas to Key West, Florida and up the Atlantic Seaboard as far as Barnegat Bay. They have owned vessels which they have operated for dive charters, fishing charters and towing services.

He has written more than 3,500 articles for magazines and newspapers.

Printed in the United States
26370LVS00002B/127-171